Second Edition

Guidelines for Report Writing

Ron S. Blicq

Red River Community College
Winnipeg, Manitoba

Senior Consultant
The Roning Group

Prentice-Hall Canada Inc., Scarborough Ontario

Canadian Cataloguing in Publication Data

Blicq, Ron S. (Ron Stanley), 1925-
  Guidelines for report writing

2nd ed.
ISBN 0-13-368713-9

1. Technical writing. 2. Report writing.
I. Title.

HF5719.B55 1990   808'.0666021   C89-094330-3

Prentice-Hall, Inc., Englewood Cliffs, New Jersey
Prentice-Hall International, Inc., London
Prentice-Hall of Australia, Pty., Ltd., Sydney
Prentice-Hall of India Pvt., Ltd., New Delhi
Prentice-Hall of Japan, Inc., Tokyo
Prentice-Hall of Southeast Asia (Pte.) Ltd., Singapore
Editora Prentice-Hall do Brasil Ltda., Rio de Janeiro
Prentice-Hall Hispanoamericana, S.A., Mexico

ISBN 0-13-368713-9

Production Editor: Chelsea Donaldson
Production Coordinator: Linda Gorman
Designer: Denise Marcella
Manufacturing Buyer: Sandra Paige
Compositor: Jay Tee Graphics Ltd., Richmond Hill
Cover image: © Kam Mak/Image Bank Canada
Printed and bound in Canada by Best/Gagné Book Manufacturers

3 4 5 IG 94 93 92

Contents

PART FOUR
Formal Reports

8 The Formal Report *110*

Preface

These guidelines are intended to be used as an easy-to-consult reference handbook. They have been prepared for and tested by a wide spectrum of report writers in various disciplines, ranging from business administrators and office managers to technicians, engineers, and scientists. The tailor-made writing plans have helped their users not only to write better-organized reports, but also to write them more easily and more rapidly.

The writing plans cover the three general categories of reports written in business, government, and industry. Short reports include informal incident, field trip, job progress, and inspection reports; semiformal reports comprise laboratory reports and medium-length investigation and evaluation reports; and formal reports cover analytical and feasibility studies, as well as major investigations. The text also includes writing plans for three types of proposals, from single-page suggestions to full-length formal presentations.

All of the writing plans are based on a unique modular method of report organization, called **The Pyramid Method**, which can help report writers identify the most important information they have to convey and focus their readers' attention on it. The pyramid method then groups the remaining information into compartments which develop the report writer's case logically and coherently.

For each type of report described in the handbook, the guidelines provide:

1. An individual writing plan.
2. Detailed instructions for using the writing plan.
3. A model report (in some cases there are two examples).
4. Comprehensive comments on how each writer has used the suggested writing plan to shape his or her report.

A writing techniques section at the rear of the handbook provides useful suggestions for "sprucing up" the appearance of reports and getting better mileage from a minimum number of words. It also shows how to construct a list of references or a bibliography; present numbers, abbreviations, and metric (SI) symbols; and prepare illustrations for insertion in the report narrative.

The penultimate chapter provides advice for report writers who keystroke and edit their own reports at a computer terminal, and takes a brief look at the implications of desktop publishing.

The final chapter discusses the writer's role as part of a report production team, and offers guidelines for working smoothly with typists, illustrators, printers, and sometimes editors, all of whom may inject their expertise into the production of a report.

R.S.B.

PART ONE

A Practical Approach to Report Writing

1

How to Use
These Guidelines

There are two ways you can use these guidelines: you can read them right through from start to finish, or you can read only the parts that apply to the kind of report writing you do. As most readers will be busy people, I expect you are more likely to read selectively.

If you choose to dip into sections of the book, I recommend you follow this reading plan:

1. Turn to the Table of Contents.
2. Identify which report types listed in Parts 2, 3 and 4 (chapters 3 through 8) you write now, and place a check mark against their names. Also mark any report types you think you might have to write over the next 12 months.
3. Read chapter 2. Chapter 2 is particularly important because it describes the basic structure on which all the reports in chapters 3 through 8 are modelled.
4. Turn to each of the reports you have marked, and:
   - Read the introductory remarks and recommended writing plan.
   - Read the model report. You will find most model reports are printed on right-hand pages, and most comments on the reports are printed on the facing left-hand pages. I recommend you first read the model report right through once, and resist the temptation to glance across to the cross-referenced comments on the facing page(s). This will give you a better "feel" for the report.
   - Read the comments on the facing page(s) and cross-reference them to the report.

Note: For some reports you write, you will find an exact writing plan to use and a comparable model to follow in the guidelines. For others, you may have to search for a writing plan that approximates your needs, and then adapt it to fit your particular situation.

5. Read Part 5 (chapters 9 through 15). These chapters contain ''how to'' suggestions on report shape, appearance, language, and writing style, and so act as a reference section which you can consult at any time.

6. As a final step, turn to the reports you did not read during step 4 and:
   • Examine the writing plan for each.
   • Read the model report. (If the report writer's rationale or writing method is not clear to you, also read the comments on the facing pages.)

The individual writing plans illustrated here have been tested and used thousands of times, and are known to work well. But bear in mind that they are only *suggestions* for organizing each report. They are not hard-and-fast rules, and you can alter them to suit both your needs and those of your audience — the person or people for whom you write each report.

2

The Report Writers' Pyramid

If I asked you to tell me what you find most difficult about report writing, would one of these answers be yours?—

"Getting started."

"Organizing the information: arranging it in the proper order."

"The writing: getting the right words down on paper the first time."

You are in good company if your answer is similar to one of these. I can ask the same question of any group of business or technical report writers and always hear the same answers. And often those who say getting started also mention one of the other answers.

The ideas presented in this book will help remove some of the drudgery from report writing. They will show you how to get started, organize your thoughts, and write simply and easily. This chapter provides you with basic guidelines. Subsequent chapters demonstrate how you can apply the guidelines to various situations.

Getting Started

Dave Kowalchuk has spent two months examining his company's methods for ordering, receiving, storing, and issuing stock. He has found them to be inefficient, has investigated alternative methods, and has worked out a plan for a better system. Now he is ready to write a report describing his findings and suggestions.

But Dave is having trouble getting started. When he sits down to write, he just can't seem to find the right words. He writes a few sentences, and sometimes several paragraphs, yet each time sets them aside. He is frustrated because he feels unable to bring his message into focus.

Dave's problem is not unusual. It stems from a simple omission: he has neglected to give sufficient thought either to his reader or to the message he has to convey. What he needs to do is make two critical decisions *before* he picks up his pen. He should ask himself two questions:

1. *Who is my reader?*
2. *What do I* most *want to tell that reader?*

Identifying the Reader

If you are writing a memo report to your manager, you will know immediately who you are writing to (although you may have to give some thought to other possible readers, if your manager is likely to circulate your memo). But if your report will have a wide readership—as Dave's may well have—then you must decide who is to be your primary reader, and write for that particular person. Trying to write for a broad range of readers can be as difficult as trying to write with no particular reader in mind. In both cases you will have no focal point for your message. And without a properly defined focal point your message may be fuzzy.

How can you identify the primary reader? It is the person (or people) who will probably use or act upon the information you provide. You need not know the person by name, although it is useful if you do because then you will have a precise focal point. But you should at least know the type of person who will use your information and be able to identify the position he or she holds.

Yet simply knowing your reader is not enough. You need to carry the identification process one step further by answering four more questions:

QUESTION 1: *What does the reader want, expect, or need to hear from me?*
You have to decide whether your reader will want a simple statement of facts or a detailed explanation of circumstances and events. You also have to consider whether the reader needs to know how certain facts were derived.

QUESTION 2: *How much does the reader know already?*
The answer to this question will provide you with a starting point for your report, since there is no need to repeat information the reader already knows. (But note that your answer may be influenced by the answer to question 4.)

QUESTION 3: *What effect do I want my report to have on the reader?*
You have to decide whether the purpose of your report is to inform or to persuade. In an informative report you simply relate the

necessary facts, and then you stop. In a persuasive report you have to convince the reader to act or react, which can range from simply agreeing with a plan you propose, through ordering materials or equipment on your behalf, to authorizing a change in policies and procedures.

QUESTION 4: *Are other people likely to read my report?*
You have to consider the route your report takes before it reaches your reader, and to whom you may send copies. If the report will pass through other people's hands, then you must consider how much additional information you will have to insert to satisfy their curiosity. (At the same time you must not let your desire to satisfy additional readers deflect you from focusing on the primary reader's needs and expectations.)

In the situation described earlier, Dave Kowalchuk decides his primary reader is Maria Pavanno, who is Manager of Purchasing and Supply. He also recognizes that Maria may circulate his report to other managers, and particularly to the Vice President of the division.

Identifying the Message

Now that Dave has his primary and secondary readers clearly in mind, he has to make a second decision. This time he has to answer a single question:

What do I most want to tell my primary reader?

Dave must examine the results of his investigation and decide which results will be most useful to Maria Pavanno. His aim should be to find key information which will so spark Maria's interest that she will want to know more. For example, would she *most* want to know that:
1. The company's supply system is out-of-date and inefficient?
2. Other businesses Dave has investigated have better supply systems?
3. There are several ways the company's supply system can be improved?
4. Improvements to the company's supply system will increase efficiency?
5. Changes to the supply system will save time and money?

Although all these points are valid, Dave reasons that Maria will be most interested in knowing how to save the department time and money. As increased efficiency is the key to these savings, he decides to combine points 4 and 5 into a single message. So he writes

"Improvements to our supply system will increase efficiency and save time and money."

This becomes his *Main Message*—the information he most wants to convey to his reader, Maria Pavanno.

When you have identified both your primary reader and your main message, it helps to write them in bold letters on a separate sheet of paper and keep the sheet in front of you as you write. That way you have a constant reminder that you are writing for a particular person and have a specific purpose in mind.

Using the Pyramid Method

If you were to ask any group of managers what single piece of advice they would give new report writers, the two replies you would hear more than any others are:

"Tell me right away what I most need to know."

"Draw my attention to the results. Don't bury them so I have to hunt for them."

You can meet both of these requirements if you use the pyramid method to organize your reports. The pyramid method emphasizes the most important information by bringing it right up front, *where it will be seen.*

As its name implies, the pyramid method suggests that you organize your reports in pyramid form, as shown in Figure 2-1. The essential information (what the reader most needs to know) sits at the top of the pyramid, where it is supported by a strong base of facts and details.

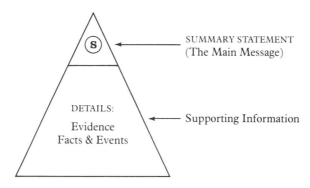

Fig. 2-1. *The report writers' pyramid.*

This concept is not new. Journalists (whom we often refer to as "reporters") have used it for decades, and in recent years experienced business and technical report writers have adopted it, because it offers them the most efficient way to communicate information.

The pyramid is used as the basic framework for organizing every type of report, although the compartments may be relabelled and expanded to suit varying situations. When you have become accustomed to using it, you will find that you automatically think "pyramid-style" every time you write.

Focusing the Message

Many beginning report writers find the pyramid method difficult to accept, because it seems to contradict what they have previously been taught. Throughout high school and into college or university they have probably been told to write using the "climactic" method. Writing climactically means developing a topic carefully, logically, and sequentially, so that the narrative leads systematically up to the main point. It is the ideal way to write an essay, short story, or mystery novel, in which the main point needs to be at the end of the piece of writing. But it does not meet the needs of business and industry, where readers want to find the Main Message at the beginning.

This does not mean that you have to completely discard the climactic method of writing: it still can be an effective way to write the Details section of a report. The pyramid method simply suggests that you identify the most important information in the Details section, and then summarize it into a short Summary Statement which you place at the front of your report. In this way you focus your readers' attention onto your Main Message.

If you have been accustomed to writing climactically, you may feel uncomfortable jumping straight into the Main Message without first gently leading up to it. To start, you can borrow a technique used by newspaper reporters.

Turn to the front page of your daily newspaper and read the first few paragraphs of each article. You will find that every article is structured the same way:

1. It has a headline, which is not really part of the article. (Normally headlines are written by editors, not the newspaper reporters who write the articles.)

2. Its opening paragraph very briefly gives you the main information—usually what has happened and, sometimes, the outcome. For example:

> Maps distributed in Ottawa yesterday show that the 77.5-tonne Skylab space station will pass directly over Winnipeg during its final days in orbit. It is expected to enter the earth's atmosphere on Wednesday July 11, plus or minus one day.

This opening paragraph is the article's Main Message, and is equivalent to the Summary Statement at the front of a short report.

3. Its remaining paragraphs expand the Main Message by providing details such as facts, events, names of places and people, dates and times, and statements by persons the reporter has interviewed. It is equivalent to the Details section of a report.

What you cannot see at the front of each article are six "hidden words," which newspaper reporters use every time they start writing. First they write

I want to tell you that...

And then they finish the sentence with their Main Message (what they most want to tell their readers). For example:

> I want to tell you that...there are larvae in the city's water supply, but local authorities say they don't pose a threat to public health.

Finally, reporters remove the six words "I want to tell you that..." (which is why they are known as "hidden words"), so that the remaining words become the article's opening sentence.

You can see how this is done if I restore the six hidden words to the front of the Skylab opening paragraph quoted earlier:

> *I want to tell you that...*maps distributed in Ottawa yesterday show that the 77.5-tonne Skylab space station will pass directly over Winnipeg during its final days in orbit.

Similarly, if you return to the front page of your daily newspaper you should find that you can also insert the six hidden words before the opening sentence of every article you read.

You can use the hidden words technique to help you start every report you write. The steps are listed on page 10.

1. Identify your reader.
2. Decide what you *most* want to tell your reader.
3. Write down the six words "I want to tell you that...."
4. Complete the sentence by writing what you have decided to tell your reader (from step 2). This is your Main Message.
5. Delete the six "hidden words" of step 3.

Here is how Dave Kowalchuk used these five steps to start his report on the company's supply system.
1. He identified his primary reader as Maria Pavanno, Manager of Purchasing and Supply.
2. He decided he wanted to tell Maria that the department needs to improve its supply system.
3. He wrote: "I want to tell you that...."
4. He finished the sentence: "...improvements to our supply system will increase efficiency and save time and money."
5. He deleted the six words he had written in step 3.

Step 4 became the opening sentence in Dave's report; that is, he used it as his Summary Statement (or Main Message). But when Dave examined the words more closely he realized that, although what he had written was accurate, as an opening statement it was too abrupt. He remembered that a Summary Statement must not only inform but also create interest and encourage the reader to continue reading. So he rearranged his information and inserted additional words to soften the abruptness. At the same time he took great care not to lose sight of his original message. After several attempts he wrote

> *(I want to tell you that...)* **My examination of our supply system shows we can increase departmental efficiency, save time, and reduce costs by improving our methods for ordering, storing, and issuing stock.**

I suggest that you, like Dave Kowalchuk, use the "hidden words" method every time you have to write a report. It will help you start more easily and ensure that you focus your readers' attention immediately onto the most important information.

Developing the Details

Because the Summary Statement of a report brings readers face-to-face with important, sometimes critical, and occasionally controversial information, it immediately triggers questions in their minds. Your responsibility is to anticipate these questions and answer them as quickly and efficiently as you can. You do this in the Details section, which amplifies and provides supportive evidence for the main message in your Summary Statement.

There are six questions a reader may ask: *Who?*, *Why?*, *Where?*, *When?*, *What?* and *How?* (See Figure 2-2.) But first you have to identify which of these questions your reader would be likely to ask. Say to yourself:

> *"If I was the intended reader, which questions would I ask after I had read only the Summary Statement?"*

(When answering this question, remember that your readers will not know the subject nearly as well as you do.)

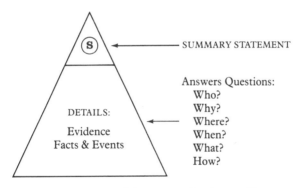

Fig. 2-2. *The base of the report writers' pyramid answers readers' questions.*

Dave Kowalchuk, for example, might say to himself: "What questions will Maria Pavanno be likely to ask immediately after she has read my Summary Statement?" (In bold type on page 10.) Dave would probably come up with the following questions:

• **Why** *(is it necessary to increase efficiency)?*

- *How (can we improve efficiency)?*
- *What (will be the effect or result of improved efficiency)?*

If he thinks that Maria wants a very detailed report, Dave might also ask:
- *When (should the improvements be implemented)?*
- *Who (will be affected by them)?*

He would omit the question *where?*, because for this report it does not need to be answered.

Now let's examine how another writer—Bev Hubka—used these six questions to develop the Details section of a short inspection report. Recently, Bev drove to a warehouse to determine the condition of some new equipment damaged in a traffic accident, and found that most of it was beyond repair. In the Summary Statement of the report Bev told her readers what they most needed to know:

> *Main Message:*   (**I want to tell you that...**) Our inspection shows that only three of the 16 microcomputers in Calvin Computer Systems shipment No. 367 can be repaired. The remainder will have to be scrapped.

To assemble facts for the Details section, Bev jotted down notes in answer to the six questions readers might ask after they had read the Summary Statement, like this:

Who *(was involved)?*
   Fran Derwood and Bev Hubka.
Why *(were you involved)?*
   We had to inspect damaged microcomputers.
   (Authority: Arlington Insurance Corporation.)
Where *(did you go)?*
   To Hillsborough Storage warehouse.
When *(did this happen)?*
   On June 13.
What *(did you find out)?*
   3 repairable micros, 13 damaged beyond repair.
How *(were they damaged)?*
   In a semitrailer involved in a highway accident.

Finally, Bev took these bare facts and shaped and expanded them into two Detail paragraphs.

Details:

Why?   We were requested by Arlington Insurance Corporation to examine the condition of 16 CANFRED microcomputers manufactured by Calvin Computer Company, Montréal, Qué. They were damaged

How?   when the semitrailer in which they were shipped overturned and

Who?   burned on a curve near Cambridge, Ont., on June 11. Fran Derwood

Where?   and I drove to Cambridge on June 13, where we were met by Arlington

When?   Insurance Corporation representative Kevin Cairns, who escorted us to the Hillsborough Storage warehouse.

What?   We found that the fire which resulted from the accident has irreparably damaged 13 microcomputers. Three others suffered smoke damage, but seem to be electronically sound. They carry serial numbers 106287, 106291, and 106294. We estimate that these microcomputers will cost an average of $350.00 each to repair, for a total repair cost of $1050.00.

The pyramid method can help you organize random bits of information, just as it helped Bev Hubka. And because it helps you eliminate unessential information, it will also shorten the length of reports you write. But it is not meant to be a rigid method for organizing details. The six basic questions are intended solely as a guide, and should be used flexibly. For example:

- The questions do not have to be answered in any particular order. You can arrange the answers in any sequence you like, balancing your personal preference against the reader's needs and the most suitable way to present your information.

- Only the appropriate questions need to be answered (i.e. the questions that are pertinent to each particular reporting situation).

- The first four questions in the list (*who?*, *why?*, *where?* and *when?*) require fairly straightforward answers. The last two questions (*what?* and *how?*) can have widely varying answers, depending on the event or situation you are reporting. This is where you explain what has happened, how it happened, what needs to be done, and possibly how best to go about it. Consequently there is ample scope for originality and ingenuity on your part.

Expanding the Details Section

The pyramid method provides the basic structure for all reports, regardless of their length. It can be used for one-paragraph reports, one-page reports, and 100-page reports. In every case the reports open with a Summary (or Summary Statement), which presents a synopsis of the main information to be conveyed (that is, the Main Message). It is followed by a longer section containing factual details, which support and amplify the initial statement.

Bev Hubka's report describing the inspection of damaged microcomputers is a typical short report structured using the simple two-part pyramid. For reports of greater length or complexity, however, the Details section at the base of the pyramid needs to be developed further. This development is obtained by expanding the Details section into three basic compartments of information:

- A **Background** compartment, which describes the circumstances leading up to the situation or event. (It answers the first four questions: *who?*, *why?*, *where?*, and *when?*)

- A **Facts & Events** compartment, which describes in detail what happened, or what you found out during your project. (It answers the last two questions: *what?* and *how?*)

- An **Outcome** compartment, which describes the results of the event or project, and sometimes suggests what action needs to be taken. (It also can answer the questions *what?* and *how?*)

The compartments are shown within the pyramid in Figure 2-3 and are keyed to the appropriate parts of the short report in Figure 2-4.

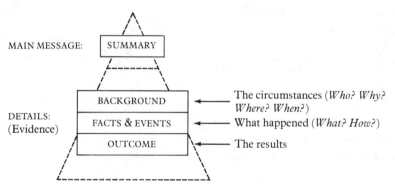

Fig. 2-3. *The main compartments of a report.*

SUMMARY

BACKGROUND
Answers
Questions:
    Who?
    When?
    Why?

FACTS
& EVENTS
Answers
Questions:
    How?
    What?

OUTCOME
Answers
Questions:
    How?
    What?

To: Don Shwenck, Marketing Manager,
            Head Office

From: Carl Peebles, Manager, Store No. 6

(*I want to tell you that...*) The installation instructions included with Vancourt BK-7 door locksets contain errors which should be corrected before any further locksets are sold.

The Vancourt BK-7 is a newly designed lockset which replaces the popular BK-6. We received our first shipment on October 12 and had sold nine of them by October 19, before we realized they were apparently faulty. By then, six customers had returned their new locksets with the complaint that they could not be installed.

I tried installing one of the returned locksets and discovered that the drilling template provided with the kit is inaccurate. There are two errors:

1. The hole for inserting the lockset through the door should be drilled to be 67 mm in diameter, not the 40 mm diameter scribed on the template.

2. The hole should be centred 73 mm from the door edge, not the specified 55 mm.

We have drawn a new template (see attachment) and have inserted a copy into every BK-7 lockset kit in our stock. We have also telephoned Vancourt Manufacturing Company to inform them of the error. I suggest that our other stores should be warned of this error and told how to correct the instructions supplied with any BK-7 locksets they have in stock.

Fig. 2-4.   *A short report structured pyramid style. The main report writing compartments are identified on the left side of the report.*

These four compartments

SUMMARY
BACKGROUND
FACTS & EVENTS
OUTCOME

provide the basic framework for every report you are likely to write. You will be able to identify them in every report described in chapters 3 through 8, although often you will find the compartments are relabelled to suit particular situations. In longer reports the compartments are also subdivided to accommodate a greater bulk of information and to improve internal organization. These subdivisions occur mostly in the Facts & Events compartment.

PART TWO

Informal Reports

3

Incident, Field Trip, and Inspection Reports

The reports in this chapter are short, each containing one to three pages of narrative and occasionally attachments such as drawings, photographs, and calculations. They are all structured using the report writers' pyramid described in chapter 2, with the pyramid modified slightly and relabelled to suit varying situations.

For each type of report described here and in subsequent chapters, the guidelines comprise:

- A description of the report, an illustration of its pyramid structure, and definitions of each writing compartment.
- One or two examples of a typical report, printed on right-hand pages.
- Comments on how the particular type of report should be or has been written, with cross-references to the example. These comments appear on the left-hand pages that face the sample reports.

Short reports such as these are most often written in memorandum form, sometimes as letters, and occasionally as semiformal reports with a title at the top of the page. For examples of typical formats, see chapter 9.

Incident Reports

An incident report (sometimes referred to as an occurrence report) describes an event that has happened, explains how and why it occurred, and indicates what effect the event had and what has been done about it. It may also suggest that corrective action be taken, or what should be done to prevent the event from recurring.

The writing compartments are similar to those of the basic report writers' pyramid, and are shown in Figure 3-1.

- The **Background** compartment answers the questions *Who?*, *Why?*, *Where?* and *When?*

- The **Event** and **Outcome** compartments answer the questions *How?* and *What?*

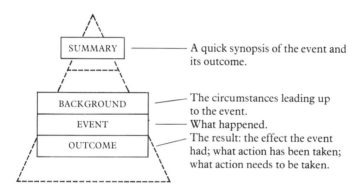

Fig. 3-1. *Writing compartments for an incident report.*

The depth of detail provided in each compartment depends on the importance of the event and how much the reader wants or needs to know about it. For example, if you were informing your comptroller of an accounting error that caused a supplier to be overpaid $100, you would write just a brief report. But if you were describing an accident which hospitalized two employees and cost $30 000 in repair work, you would be expected to write a detailed report that fully described the circumstances and the corrective action that had been taken.

The comments on page 20 identify the four writing compartments in the short incident report on page 21.

Incident Report
Reporting a Pricing Error

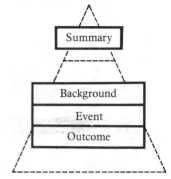

Comments

In the report on the opposite page, Paul Willis, an assistant manager at O'Connell's Department Store, is describing a pricing error to Jim Knox, his manager.

(1) In his **Summary Statement** Paul explains very briefly what happened and the effect it had. (Notice that the hidden words "I want to tell you that…" can be placed not only in front of this paragraph, but in front of *all* paragraphs. This is not unusual for a short report.)

(2) In his **Background** compartment Paul answers the four questions his reader (Jim Knox) is likely to ask:
>   *What* barbecues were they? (Cranston CBQ)
>   *When* did this happen? (Today)
>   *How* did it happen? (Details of error)
>   *Who* was responsible? ("I": Paul)

Notice how the words "They were…" build a successful transition between Paul's Summary Statement and the beginning of the Background compartment.

(3) The **Event** compartment describes exactly what happened and explains why the event could not have been averted (it answers the question *Why?*).

(4) In his **Outcome** compartment Paul answers the question: *What* did you do about it?

Paul has a choice regarding the position of the last sentence of paragraph 2, in which he explains how the printing error occurred. Alternatively, he could include it as part of paragraph 4 (Outcome), on the assumption that it is information he obtained after the event.

As a report writer you will sometimes encounter situations like this, in which you have to decide where to place a particular piece of information. You should base your choice on what feels most comfortable from both your own point of view and that of the report reader.

MEMORANDUM

From: Paul Willis   Date: March 31, 19xx

To: J Knox, Manager   Subject: Pricing Error
       Electrical Appliances

① An advertising error has forced us to sell 30 electric barbecues at $54.00 below the planned sale price, for a total loss of $1620.00.

② They were Cranston model CBQ barbecues which are regularly sold for $229.95. They were to be reduced to $182.95 for today's personal shopping Yellow Tag sale. However, last night's newspaper advertisement displayed a sale price of only $128.95. The error occurred during typesetting, and I did not notice it when I OK'd the proof yesterday afternoon.

③ All 30 barbecues on the floor had to be sold at the advertised price because they were claimed by customers within two minutes of door opening, before we were aware of the error.

④ I immediately posted a "sold out" sign, and have inserted a price correction in this afternoon's newspaper.

Paul

Trip Reports

Trip reports are written whenever people leave their usual place of work to do something elsewhere. Their reports can cover many kinds of events, such as:

• Installation or modification of equipment.

• Assistance on a field project.

• Attendance at a conference, seminar, or workshop.

• Repairs to a client's equipment or field instruments.

• Evaluation of another firm's buildings, facilities, or methods.

Whatever the circumstances, the writing compartments for a field trip report are essentially the same as those for the basic report writing pyramid described in chapter 2. The Event compartment, however, is relabelled THE JOB, as shown in Figure 3-2.

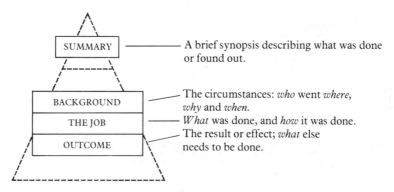

Fig. 3-2.   *Writing compartments for a trip report.*

These compartments generally contain the following information:

- The **Background** compartment describes the purpose of the trip, mentions on whose authority it was taken, and lists circumstantial details such as the names of people involved, and dates and locations.
- The **Job** compartment describes what was done. Often, it can be broken down into four subcompartments:
  1. What the reporter writer set out to do.
  2. What was actually done.
  3. What could not be done, and why.
  4. What else was done.

  The fourth subcompartment is necessary because people on field trips often find themselves doing things beyond the purpose of their assignment. For example, a technician sent to repair a defective diesel power unit at a remote radar site may be asked by the on-site staff to look at a second unit that is "running rough," and spend an additional six hours adjusting its timing cycle. The time spent on this additional work must be accounted for, and the work must be described in the trip report.

- The **Outcome** compartment sums up the results of the trip and, if further work still needs to be done or follow-up action should be taken, suggests what is necessary and even how and by whom it should be accomplished.

Many trip reports are short and simply follow the compartment arrangement in a few paragraphs, as shown in the examples on pages 25 and 27. Some longer, more detailed trip reports may need headings to break up the narrative into visible compartments. Typical headings might be:

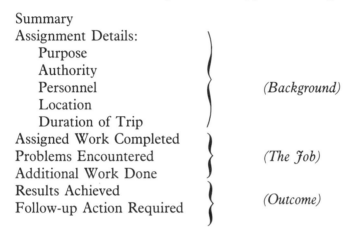

Summary
Assignment Details:
    Purpose
    Authority
    Personnel   *(Background)*
    Location
    Duration of Trip
Assigned Work Completed
Problems Encountered   *(The Job)*
Additional Work Done
Results Achieved
Follow-up Action Required   *(Outcome)*

Trip reports are often submitted as memorandums, written by the person who made the trip (or who was in charge of a group of people who did the job as a team), and addressed to the appropriate supervisor or manager. It is natural, therefore, to use the first person for such reports—"I" if the writer was alone, or "we" if several people were involved. This personalization of short memorandum or letter reports is encouraged because it helps report writers sound confident. The first person has been used in both example trip reports that follow, which comprise:

- a report on a field installation (page 25), and
- a report on seminar attendance (page 27).

A method for adapting trip report compartments so they can be used to report conference attendance is suggested on page 28.

Trip Report No. 1
Reporting an Installation

Comments

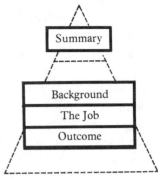

Frank Crane is a field service representative for Vancourt Business Systems Inc. He is reporting an installation he has just completed to his company's R & D Manager, Dale Rogerson.

(1) For his **Summary Statement** (opposite) Frank has picked information primarily from the Background and Job compartments.

(2) The **Background** compartment brings together all the bits and pieces of information relating to the trip. (It answers the questions: *Who went where, why, and when?*)

Note that Frank has spent some time describing the purpose of the modification kit, so that readers not familiar with it will be better able to understand his report.

(3) The **Job** compartment starts here.

For a trip report describing installation, modification, or repair work, the following guidelines provide a useful rule of thumb:

- Describe routine work that goes according to plan as briefly as possible, particularly if there is an instruction or work specification which can be referred to and/or attached.
- Describe unexpected work, unusual events, or problems in some
(4)   detail, and particularly explain how a difficult situation has been resolved.

(5) *Note:* To conserve space in this book, the diagram and invoice have been omitted.

(6) Sometimes it can be difficult to identify exactly where the **Outcome** compartment starts. Some people might say it starts at the beginning of the previous paragraph; others might say it starts at this paragraph; while still others might argue it starts at the next paragraph. Only Frank really needs to know where the Outcome starts (because he uses it to organize his report). All that is necessary from the reader's point of

view is that the report read smoothly and progress logically from beginning to end.

(7) In this final **Outcome** statement, Frank provides a "memory-jogger" for his readers. In effect he is saying to both Dale Rogerson (to whom the report is addressed) and Jerry Morganski (who receives a copy), "Take note! Plan to send someone to Westland between January 20 & 24."

VANCOURT BUSINESS SYSTEMS INC

From: Frank Crane, Field Service Rep.   Date: October 23, 19xx

To: Dale Rogerson, Manager   Subject: Installation of Prototype
Research and Development   Modification Kit MCR-1

① An MCR-1 multi-account readout display and control box have been installed on a model 261 Processor, where they will be field-tested for three months.

② I was assigned by Work Order M97 to install the prototype kit on a processor owned by Arrow Industries at Westland, where arrangements had been made for it to be field-evaluated. Modification kit MCR-1 permits raw data on individual accounts stored in Vancourt 261 Processors to be made instantly available on a miniature display unit mounted beside the processor. I drove to Westland on October 19 and returned on October 22.

③ The circuit and control box were installed without difficulty. However, a locally manufactured equipment rack on which the 261 Processor has been mounted prevented installation of the miniature display unit beside the processor, as directed in step 29 of the installation specification.

④ I arranged for the mounting tray to be modified by Corwin Metals in Westland, so that it could be mounted on top of the processor as shown on the attached diagram. Corwin Metals' invoice for $116.25
⑤ is attached.

⑥ I tested the control box and miniature display unit, and detected and corrected two display faults. I then tested the installation for three more hours, but detected no further faults. During this period I trained three employees of Arrow Industries to use the equipment.

Their contact employee will be Lorne Carter, who is one of the three persons I trained, and with whom I left evaluation and serviceability status report forms. He will mail these to you weekly.

⑦ Arrangements will have to be made to disconnect and remove the kit during the week of January 20 to 24, 19xx.

Frank Crane

FC:jp

cc Jerry Morganski, Field Service Manager

Trip Report No. 2
Reporting Seminar Attendance

Comments

Personnel assistant Karen Young has recently attended a seminar and is evaluating it in a report (opposite) to the Personnel Manager, Audrey Rivers.

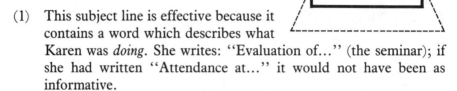

(1)   This subject line is effective because it contains a word which describes what Karen was *doing*. She writes: "Evaluation of..." (the seminar); if she had written "Attendance at..." it would not have been as informative.

(2)   Karen's enthusiastic **Summary Statement** is drawn primarily from the Outcome compartment [see (5)].

(3)   This **Background** compartment does three things:
  • It describes the seminar.
  • It outlines Karen's involvement in it.
  • It answers the questions *Who?*, *Why?*, *Where?*, and *When?*

(4)   Karen divides the **Job** compartment into two subcompartments:

(4A) • A brief description of how the seminar was organized and, by implication, what she did as a seminar participant.

(4B) • An evaluation of the seminar's effectiveness and usefulness.

(5)   For this type of report, the **Outcome** compartment is particularly important because it provides an answer to the question "Was the purpose of the trip achieved?" Karen's manager wants to know how good the seminar is, and Karen has told her confidently that the company should buy the in-house version of it, and has even suggested that she could be workshop leader for it.

Note: Page 28 contains suggestions for using these writing compartments to report attendance at a conference or meeting.

MEMORANDUM

To: Audrey Rivers   From: Karen Young
     Personnel Manager   Personnel Assistant

Date: March 19, 19xx   Subject: Evaluation of Roning
                                      Group "Meetings" Seminar (1)

(2) The Roning Group "Meetings" seminar is thoroughly worth attending and
should be made available to all supervisory employees.

The attached folder describes the seminar in detail. Its full title is
"Increasing the Effectiveness of Business Meetings" and it is available
in two formats: as a public seminar such as the one I attended, and as
a kit for in-house presentation. Attendance at a public seminar costs
(3) $35.00 per person. The kit, which contains sufficient materials to
train 48 employees, costs $600.00, which is equivalent to $12.50 per
person.

The seminar I attended was held at the downtown Holiday Inn from 1:00
to 4:30 p.m. yesterday, March 18. I was selected to attend so that I
could evaluate its suitability for in-house use.

(4) The seminar was divided into three one-hour compartments.

1. For the first hour the seminar leader demonstrated techniques for
    improving meeting performance, and then we prepared to take part
    in two meetings. We were divided into two groups, and we were
    each given two roles to play.

(4A) 2. During the second hour the first group held a meeting, and the
    second group evaluated performance on a one-to-one basis.

3. During the third hour the groups' roles were reversed. The semi-
    nar leader also summed up after each meeting and pointed out our
    strengths and weaknesses.

I found the seminar to be an excellent learning experience. The
atmosphere was relaxed, the participants were actively involved for
more than 75% of the time and had realistic, recognizable roles to
(4B) play, and the topics for the two meetings were both interesting and
relevant. Of particular value were the comments we could make on
one another's performance as meeting participants.

I suggest that we purchase The Roning Group's "Meetings" kit and use
(5) it to help our managers and supervisors hold more efficient meetings.
The experience I gained at yesterday's seminar has prepared me
sufficiently to run in-house workshops.

Karen

Reporting Conference Attendance

The trip report compartments can be used to describe attendance at a conference or meeting. The most difficult one to write is the Job compartment, and the most efficient way to organize it is to divide it into subcompartments that focus on:

- what the person attending the conference expected to gain, learn, or find out,
- what the programme promised would be covered,
- what sessions were attended, and why they were chosen (this is important for a conference with several simultaneous sessions),
- what was gained or learned by attending these sessions,
- what was gained or learned from meeting and talking to other persons attending the conference, and
- what other activities were attended.

Inspection Reports

An inspection report is similar to a field trip report, in that its writer has usually gone somewhere to inspect something. Bev Hubka's trip to Cambridge to inspect damaged microcomputers is an example (see chapter 2).

Other typical situations requiring an inspection report to be written include:

- Examination of a building to determine its suitability as a storage facility.
- Inspection of construction work, such as a bridge, building, or road.
- Checks of manufactured items, to assure they are of the required quality.
- Inspection of goods ordered for a job, to check that the necessary quantities and correct items have been received.

The writing compartments are also similar to those for a trip report, except that the compartment previously labelled simply as "The Job" can be more clearly defined as "Findings." The report writing pyramid is illustrated in Figure 3-3.

The following notes suggest what these compartments should contain and how the information should be arranged.

- The **Background** compartment describes the purpose of the inspection, mentions on whose authority it was performed, and lists circumstantial details such as the names of people involved and the date and location of the inspection.

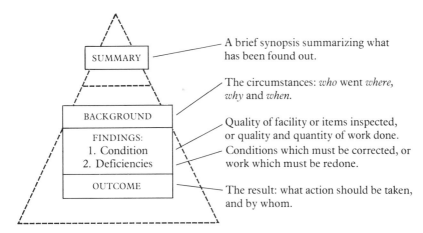

Fig. 3-3. *Writing compartments for an inspection report.*

• The **Findings** compartment can often be divided into two subcompartments, one of which describes *conditions found*, while the other lists *deficiencies* (a deficiency can be either an unacceptable condition or a missing item). The length and complexity of the findings will dictate how these compartments are organized. Short, simple findings can be arranged in this order:

> Conditions Found:
>   1. _____
>   2. _____
>   3. _____(etc)
>
> Deficiencies:
>   1. _____
>   2. _____(etc)

This arrangement is illustrated in Inspection Report No. 1 [see items (4) and (5) on page 33]. Longer, more complex findings should be arranged so that the deficiencies for each item are listed immediately after the item's condition has been described.

> Inspection Findings:
>   Item A:
>   Condition
>   Deficiencies
>   Item B:
>   Condition
>   Deficiencies (etc)

This arrangement is shown in Inspection Report No. 2 [see items (4), (5), and (6) on page 34]. The intention is to keep the deficiencies reasonably close to the condition from which they evolve.

You would be wise to use a miniature pyramid to organize the information in each of the Conditions Found and Deficiencies subcompartments, as shown in Figure 3-4.

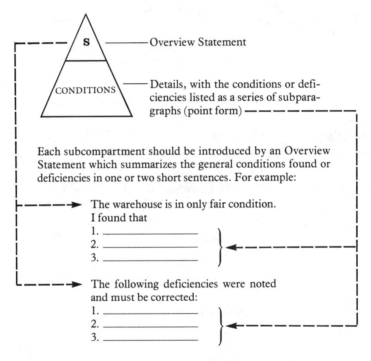

Fig. 3-4. *Organization of the* Conditions Found *and* Deficiencies *subcompartments.*

- The **Outcome** compartment suggests what should be done as a result of the inspection. If deficiencies have been listed at the end of the previous compartment, the outcome is likely to be short. For example:

    Providing the deficiencies I have listed are corrected, the warehouse should make a suitable storage facility for the Passant Project.

The two inspection reports on the following pages demonstrate how these guidelines are applied. Notice particularly how the use of the first person (''I'') is employed by both writers, but it occurs more often and more naturally in the report prepared as a memorandum (report No. 2).

A basic form for recording inspection information is shown in Figure 3-5.

INSPECTION REPORT

Location: _____	Date: _____
Item(s) being inspected:	
Inspector: _____	Contractor: _____

CONDITIONS FOUND:

DEFICIENCIES:

RECOMMENDATION(S):

Fig. 3-5. *A form for an inspection report.*

Inspection Report No. 1
Inspecting a Contractor's Work

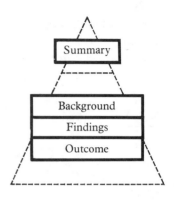

Comments

(1) Paul Thorvaldson, the author of the report on the opposite page, has chosen to use a slightly more formal format than a memorandum would offer. He reasons that several people will read the report, and the contractor will probably be given a copy when asked to rectify the deficiencies.

(2) The **Summary Statement** tells readers right away what they most want to know—that the new facility is ready.

(3) In the **Background** compartment, Paul describes the details leading up to his inspection visit. He answers the questions *Who?*, *Where?*, *When?*, and *Why?*

(4) The **Findings** compartment starts here with an overview statement ("The contractor has done a good job"). It continues immediately with the **Conditions Found** subcompartment, which Paul limits to two short sentences mentioning the main items he noticed. When specifications have been met, there is no need to describe everything that has been done; it is sufficient simply to indicate the job has been completed correctly. But when specifications have not been met, attention must be drawn to every item which has been improperly done [see (5)].

(5) The **Findings** compartment continues with the **Deficiencies**. Each item needing correction is listed in a separate subparagraph (to make it easy to identify step-by-step what action has to be taken), and in clearcut terms which will not be misunderstood.

If there are many deficiencies it may be more convenient to list them on a separate sheet or sheets (called an attachment), and to refer to them in the Deficiencies paragraph.

> The 27 deficiencies listed on the attached sheets must be corrected by the contractor before the job can be accepted.

(6) The **Outcome** compartment describes the result of the inspection (in this case, whether the contractor's work can be accepted and the new accommodation occupied). The Outcome compartment provided Paul with the primary information he needed for the summary at the start of his report.

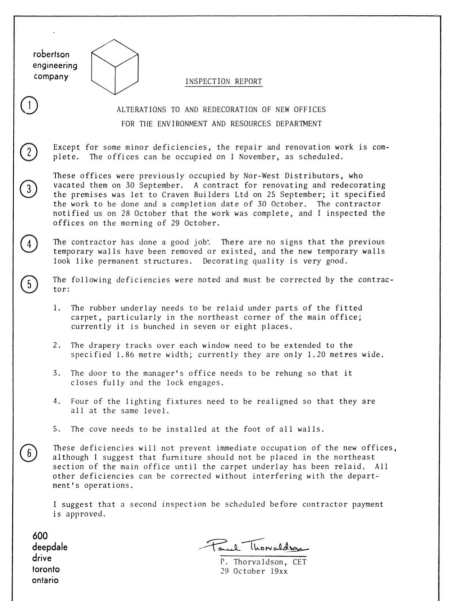

robertson
engineering
company

INSPECTION REPORT

(1)

ALTERATIONS TO AND REDECORATION OF NEW OFFICES
FOR THE ENVIRONMENT AND RESOURCES DEPARTMENT

(2)
Except for some minor deficiencies, the repair and renovation work is complete. The offices can be occupied on 1 November, as scheduled.

(3)
These offices were previously occupied by Nor-West Distributors, who vacated them on 30 September. A contract for renovating and redecorating the premises was let to Craven Builders Ltd on 25 September; it specified the work to be done and a completion date of 30 October. The contractor notified us on 28 October that the work was complete, and I inspected the offices on the morning of 29 October.

(4)
The contractor has done a good job. There are no signs that the previous temporary walls have been removed or existed, and the new temporary walls look like permanent structures. Decorating quality is very good.

(5)
The following deficiencies were noted and must be corrected by the contractor:

1. The rubber underlay needs to be relaid under parts of the fitted carpet, particularly in the northeast corner of the main office; currently it is bunched in seven or eight places.

2. The drapery tracks over each window need to be extended to the specified 1.86 metre width; currently they are only 1.20 metres wide.

3. The door to the manager's office needs to be rehung so that it closes fully and the lock engages.

4. Four of the lighting fixtures need to be realigned so that they are all at the same level.

5. The cove needs to be installed at the foot of all walls.

(6)
These deficiencies will not prevent immediate occupation of the new offices, although I suggest that furniture should not be placed in the northeast section of the main office until the carpet underlay has been relaid. All other deficiencies can be corrected without interfering with the department's operations.

I suggest that a second inspection be scheduled before contractor payment is approved.

600
deepdale
drive
toronto
ontario

Paul Thorvaldson
P. Thorvaldson, CET
29 October 19xx

Inspection Report No. 2
Inspecting Printing Equipment

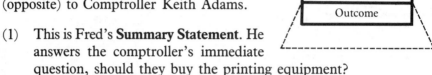

Comments

Fred Parkin has been examining some used printing equipment his company is considering buying, and reports his findings (opposite) to Comptroller Keith Adams.

(1)   This is Fred's **Summary Statement**. He answers the comptroller's immediate question, should they buy the printing equipment?

(2)   In the **Background** compartment Fred answers the questions *Who?*, *Where?*, *When?*, and *Why?* He gives more detail than the Comptroller probably needs because he is aware that other management persons who may be involved in the decision may not know the circumstances.

(3)   The **Findings** compartment starts with a comment on the equipment's overall condition. An overview statement like this prepares the reader for the specific details that follow. The findings continue through the remainder of the report, except for the final paragraph.

(4)   Fred has chosen to treat each major piece of equipment separately, and to comment on both its condition and deficiencies under the one heading.

(5A) to (5D)   These comprise the **Conditions Found** subcompartment for each major piece of equipment. The Comptroller would not expect Fred to give a detailed description of each.

(6A) to (6D)   These are the major **Deficiencies** for each piece of equipment. They are not listed as specific, item-by-item deficiencies because it would have taken much time and effort for Fred to prepare a detailed list. To do so would seem particularly pointless when Fred is suggesting they do not buy the equipment.

(6B)   This is an unusual "deficiency." Rather than state what action would have to be taken, it comments on the suitability of the equipment compared to more modern systems.

(7)   The **Outcome** compartment on page 2 of the report sums up Fred's
feelings about the proposed purchase. It was from this paragraph
that Fred drew most of the information for his summary [at (1)].

H. L. Winman and Associates

INTER - OFFICE MEMORANDUM

From: Fred Parkin   Date: May 20, 19xx

To: Keith Adams, Comptroller   Subject: Inspection of Cam Industries'
                                                              Printing Equipment

(1)   Although Cam Industries is selling their printing equipment at a very
attractive price, I would hesitate to buy any of it.

(2)   As requested in your memo of May 17, I visited Cam Industries at 2820
Wampole Road this morning to inspect their printing facility. They will
be closing their in-house print shop on June 30 and will be selling all
the equipment for $15 000, or individual items for a total of $17 500.
I was to examine the equipment and consider whether all of it, or individual items, would make a practicable purchase for the facility we plan
to set up to print parts lists and brochures.

(3)   I found the printing equipment to be in only fair condition. Most of it
has been in use for more than 12 years, and seems to have been operated
by untrained help. The condition of major items is outlined briefly
below:

(4)   Bellweather 316 Offset Duplicator

(5A)   This unit is 15 years old but looks like 20! Service has been
erratic, with service reps being called in only upon equipment
failure (the present owners apparently do not believe in preven-
tive maintenance).

(6A)   I estimate that almost all moving parts will have to be replaced
immediately or very shortly, for a total repair cost of $6000.
This was confirmed by the local Bellweather service rep, who knows
the equipment.

Flexite 60 Camera and Mounting Frame

(5B)   The unit is 12 years old and is in generally good condition. It
has no moving parts, so no noticeable wear has taken place. The
camera bellows seem to be satisfactory but probably should be inspected professionally. At $1600 the unit is an excellent buy.

(6B)   But it remains an antiquated, slow system to use when compared to
newer systems which are more efficient and have much greater
flexibility.

2/ ...

2

Fortnum "Platitude 212" Platemaker

(5C) The platemaker is in poor condition. It has evidently been dropped or something heavy has been dropped on it, for the surface is dented and severely scratched. Whether the interior has been similarly damaged cannot be assessed without dismantling the unit.

(5D) Repair or replacement (by a second-hand unit) would cost at least $3800.

Collator, Binders, Staplers, Padders, etc

(6C) There is an assortment of equipment in varying condition, with a total sale value of $900. About half could be retained, but (6D) the remainder would have to be repaired or replaced at a cost of $1600.

(7) If we purchase Cam Industries' printing equipment for $15 000, we will almost immediately have to invest a further $11 400 for repairs and replacement items, and even then we will own outdated equipment which is at least 12 years old. I believe this would be an uneconomical purchase.

4

Progress Reports and Short Investigation Reports

Like the reports in chapter 3, these informal reports are also short, seldom exceeding three pages plus attachments. Their writing compartments, however, are often expanded to include more subdivisions, particularly in the Facts & Events compartment of the basic pyramid (Figure 2-3).

When a report contains detailed information, such as lists of materials, cost analyses, schedules, or drawings, they are normally removed from the body of the report (from the Facts & Events compartment) and placed at the back, where they are referred to as "Attachments" or "Appendices." (This is done to avoid cluttering the report narrative with tabular data and thus interrupting reading continuity.) Because they provide supportive evidence, or "back up," for statements made in the report, a separate compartment is created for them at the foot of the report writers' pyramid. This compartment is labelled **Back-up** and is shown with a dotted line in Figure 4-1 to indicate that it is optional.

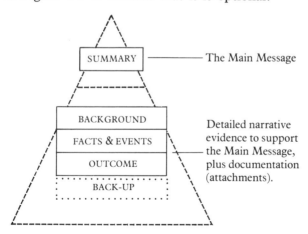

Fig. 4-1. *The report writers' pyramid with a back-up compartment for attachments and appendices.*

Progress Reports

Progress reports keep management informed of work progress on projects that span a lengthy period, which can vary from a few weeks for a small manufacturing contract to several years for construction of a hydroelectric power station and transmission system.

There are two types of progress reports:

• Occasional progress reports are written at random intervals and usually concern shorter-length projects.

• Periodic progress reports are written at regular intervals (usually weekly, biweekly, or monthly), and concern projects spanning several months or years.

The writing compartments are the same for both reports, although there are differences in their application. They evolve from the basic report writing pyramid, with two of the compartments relabelled to suit a progress-reporting situation (see Figure 4-2).

• **Progress** replaces the basic Facts & Events compartment, and is subdivided into four smaller compartments describing:

1. Planned work.
2. Work done.
3. Problems encountered.
4. Adherence to schedule.

• **Plans** replaces the original Outcome compartment. There is also an optional **Back-up** compartment, for assembling forms and statistical data pertinent to the project.

These compartments are described in more detail on the following pages, with references to the two progress reports between pages 41 and 49.

Occasional Progress Report

Occasional progress reports apply to short projects during which only one progress report will probably be necessary. Sometimes they are written near the mid-project point. Occasionally they are written to forewarn management that problems have occurred and delays can be expected. But most often they are written as soon as the project leader has a sufficiently clear picture of work progress to confidently predict a firm project completion date.

The report writing compartments for an occasional progress report are shown in Figure 4-2 and then discussed in more detail.

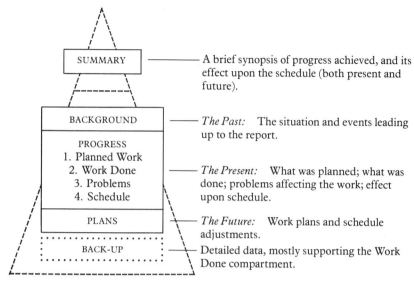

Fig. 4-2. *Writing compartments for a progress report.*

Summary

The summary should comment briefly on the progress achieved and whether the project is on schedule; it may also predict a project completion date. Its information is drawn from the Work Done, Schedule, and Plans compartments.

Background

If the report will be read only by people familiar with the project, then only minimum background information is necessary. But if it will also be circulated to other readers, then the Background compartment should describe briefly the people involved in the project, and the location and dates (i.e. it should answer the questions *Who?*, *Where?*, *Why?*, and *When?*).

Progress

The Progress compartment contains information from the four subcompartments illustrated in Figure 4-2, which are normally arranged in the order shown (although it is not uncommon for some of these subcompartments to overlap or be omitted).

- The **Planned Work** subcompartment outlines what work should have been completed by the reporting date. Normally only a brief statement, it can refer to an attached schedule or work plan.

- The **Work Done** subcompartment describes how much work has been completed. Only brief comments are necessary for work that has gone smoothly and has progressed as planned. If lengthy numerical data has to be included, it should be placed in an attachment rather than inserted in the report narrative. More detailed comments should be provided if there have been variances from the work plan. They should explain why the variances were necessary and any unusual action that was taken.

- The **Problems** subcompartment comprises events or situations which affected the *doing* of the job (e.g. a blizzard that stopped work for two days, late delivery of essential parts, or a strike which prevented access to necessary data). These problems should be described in detail, and the explanation should include what action was taken to overcome each problem and how successful the action was.

- The **Schedule** subcompartment states whether the project is ahead of, on, or behind schedule. If ahead of or behind schedule, the difference should be quoted in hours, days, or weeks.

Plans

This usually short compartment describes the report writer's plans and expectations for the remainder of the project. It should indicate whether the project will finish on schedule and, if not, predict a revised completion date. There should be an obvious link between this compartment and the previous subcompartment (Schedule).

Back-up

The optional Back-up compartment contains data such as drawings, statistics, specifications, and results of tests, which if included with the earlier parts of the report would tend to clutter the report narrative. This supporting information is grouped and placed in attachments. Each attachment must be referred to in the Background or Progress section of the report, so that the reader will know it is there.

These compartments are identified in Progress Report No. 1, on the following two pages.

Progress Report No. 1
Occasional Progress Report

Comments

Marjorie Franckel has been delayed in carrying out environmental studies in the Yukon and reports her progress (page 42) to Vic Braun, her manager. Her progress report, which was originally handwritten because she had no access to a typewriter, has been typed for insertion in these guidelines.

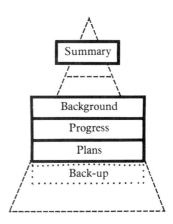

(1) This is the **Summary Statement**, and it reports mainly that Marjorie's study is running behind schedule.

(2) This **Background** compartment also includes planned work. In an informal report written under such difficult conditions, Marjorie could have been forgiven if she had omitted this paragraph. She has included it because she knows that Vic Braun (her department manager) probably will have her report typed and sent to the Department of Transport.

(3) The **Progress** compartment starts here and continues to the middle of the paragraph labelled (6). The **Work Done** subcompartment also starts here and continues to the end of (5). Quoting facts and figures, as Marjorie has done in the three subparagraphs, makes a report writer sound confident and knowledgeable.

(4) The attached map becomes the **Back-up** compartment. (It has been omitted from this copy of the report to conserve space.)

(5) See note (3).

(6) In this **Problems** subcompartment, Marjorie outlines why part of her report is rather vague and why the study has been delayed.

(7) The **Schedule** subcompartment is this single, rather indefinite sentence. Marjorie cannot be more exact because she simply does not know how long it will take to find and interview people.

(8) This final paragraph is the **Plans** compartment.

H. L. Winman and Associates

INTER - OFFICE MEMORANDUM

From: Marjorie Franckel, Biologist

Date: August 18, 19xx

To: Vic Braun, Manager
Environmental Studies

Subject: Progress: Study of
Caribou Calving Grounds

(1) My study of the calving areas used by the Porcupine herd of caribou has been delayed by lack and inaccessibility of data. I doubt whether I will be able to complete the study before September 15.

(2) The study is being done for the Department of Transport, to determine the boundaries and dates of calving so that specific areas can be designated as "Restricted Flying Zones" during the calving season. Currently I am working out of Old Crow in the Yukon.

(3) I have defined the eastern and western limits of the North Slope calving area bordering the Beaufort Sea (see attached map), and have identified three approach routes used by the caribou during their northbound spring migration. These are: (4)

   1. Through the Richardson Mountains in the east, along the Yukon/Northwest Territories border.

   2. Through the Brooks Range of mountains north of Old Crow.

   3. Through the Brooks Range in Alaska, between the Canning River and the Yukon border.

(5) In normal years most calving seems to take place in the Arctic Wildlife Refuge in Alaska between early May and early June. But if bad travel conditions delay the migration, calving occurs farther east along the coastal plain or sometimes even in the mountain ranges while the herd is still migrating.

(6) My problem has been to identify which migration routes are most used, clear-cut dates when calving occurs, and the earliest and latest dates that the caribou have been known to enter the coastal plain. Only a few residents have observed calving, and I have been trying to identify who they are and to interview them. This lack of real information has delayed (7) my study by at least 15 days.

(8) For the next two or three weeks I will be travelling with an interpreter to interview Inuit in very small communities north of Old Crow and as far east as Aklavik. During this period it is unlikely you will be able to contact me.

"Marjorie"

Periodic Progress Report

The compartments for a periodic progress report contain similar information to those for an occasional progress report, but there is some shift in content and emphasis.

The format of a periodic progress report also appears to be more rigid than that of an occasional report. This rigidity is imposed not so much by established rules as by the content and shape of the initial report in a series. The implication is important: report writers should take great care in planning a progress report which is to be the first of a series because they will be expected to conform to the same shape in successive reports.

The compartments outlined below are those shown in Figure 4-2. They provide useful guidelines to follow, and demonstrate the differences in content between the occasional and periodic progress reports.

Summary

The summary should comment briefly on the work accomplished during the reporting period. It may also mention whether the project is on schedule. This information can be drawn from the Work Done and Schedule compartments.

Background

Except for the first report in a series, which will be fairly detailed, the Background compartment probably will refer only to:

- the project number or identification code,
- the dates encompassing the specific reporting period, and
- the situation at the end of the previous reporting period, with particular reference to the project's position relative to the established schedule.

Progress

The Progress compartment is divided into four subcompartments. In short reports these subcompartments may interlock or overlap, but in longer reports they are more likely to be independent units. If there is no information for a particular compartment, then the compartment is omitted.

1. The **Planned Work** subcompartment outlines what should have been accomplished during the reporting period. It may refer to either the original schedule or a revised schedule defined in a previous progress report. Normally it is short, sometimes it is combined with Work Done, and occasionally it can be omitted.

2. The **Work Done** subcompartment describes what has been achieved during the reporting period. Ideally, this subcompartment will:
   - open with a brief overview statement which sums up in general terms what has been accomplished,
   - continue with a series of subparagraphs each describing in more detail what has been done on a specific aspect of the project,
   - refer to attachments containing comprehensive numerical data, statistics, or tables (see the Back-up compartment, below), and
   - explain variations from the planned work, or unusual activities affecting work progress (this may be linked with the Problems subcompartment).

3. **Problems** are factors which have caused changes in plans or in the schedule. The report should describe what action has been taken to overcome the problems, whether the action was successful, if the problems still exist, and what action will continue to be taken, either to avert the problems or to make up lost project time.

4. The **Schedule** subcompartment states whether the project was ahead of, on, or behind schedule on the last day of the reporting period. (There may be a convenient link between this compartment and the end of the previous compartment.) If ahead of or behind schedule, it should state the number of hours, days, or weeks involved. It may also predict when the project will be back on schedule, and recommend a revised schedule for the next reporting period.

Plans

This compartment is very short if the project is running smoothly and is on schedule. But if there are problems affecting the work, it should outline the report writer's expectations for the next reporting period, or even suggest a revised schedule for the whole project.

Back-up

This optional compartment is used to store detailed information such as forms containing weekly summaries of work done (e.g. yards of concrete poured, number of panels installed, length of cable strung), tests, and inspections.

Headings and Paragraph Numbering

Periodic progress reports can often benefit from the judicious use of headings and a simple paragraph numbering system. The following headings are suggested:

> Summary
> Introduction
> Project Progress
> Problems Encountered
> Adherence to Schedule:
> > Current
> > Predicted
> Attachments

A paragraph and subparagraph numbering system shows readers how the information has been organized, and provides a handy means of cross-referencing within the report and between successive reports.

The suggested numbering system uses whole numbers for paragraphs and decimals for subparagraphs. For example:

> 3. Project Progress
> > During the month we . . .   *(overview)*
> > 3.1 conducted field tests... ⎫
> > 3.2 installed three pads...   ⎬ *(specific details)*
> > 3.3 removed old cables...   ⎭

The periodic progress report which follows shows how writing compartments, headings, and a paragraph numbering system can be combined to shape a report.

Progress Report No. 2
A Periodic Progress Report

Comments

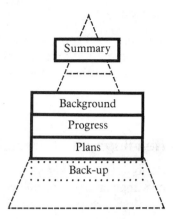

(1) Project coordinator Roger Korolick has chosen this semiformal format, rather than a memorandum, for his progress report on a trailer installation (opposite) because it will be circulated to several people, such as the divisional vice president and the marketing manager.

(2) This subheading takes the place of the **Background** compartment.

(3) Roger has taken main points from the Work Done compartment for his summary. ("Synopsis" is a lesser-used name for "summary.")

(4) The four headings and the paragraph numbering system help readers *see* how Roger has organized his report. Suggestions for using headings and paragraph numbers are on page 45.

(5) This overview statement at the start of the **Progress** compartment gives the reader a quick picture of the overall situation and introduces the details that follow.

(6) Roger's description of **Work Done** starts here and continues to the end of (7). He reports on the exterior painting first because it has been carried forward from the previous month (his May 31 report mentioned that the trailer had been taken out for painting).

(7) The remaining four items all describe work which will continue into the following months. For each, Roger finishes with a closing statement that comments on the schedule, predicts a revised completion date, or states what action will be taken, and when. This is simpler than carrying all the plans information forward and lumping it into one big compartment later in the report.

(8) The second of these "unsatisfactory conditions" introduces a problem, which Roger develops further in paragraph 3.1 (on page 2 of the report).

(9) Roger must remember to carry this item forward and comment on it in the Progress section of his July report.

VANCOURT BUSINESS SYSTEMS INC

(1)

PROGRESS REPORT No. 5 - PROJECT W16

(2)

EQUIPPING MOBILE TRAINING AND DISPLAY TRAILER

Reporting Period: June 1 to 30, 19xx

(3)

1. Synopsis

The project is generally on schedule. Trailer painting is complete, air conditioning has been installed, and work has started on wiring and positioning the work stations.

(4)

2. Work Accomplished

(5)

With the exception of the instructor's console, work has progressed well during the month. Major activity has occurred in five areas:

(6)

2.1 Exterior Painting. The 7.5 metre Fruehauf trailer, which had been taken to Display Signs Ltd on May 26, was returned on June 8 with the corporate logo and trailer identification painted on both sides and the back.

(7)

2.2 Individual Learning Centres. The first three of the six carrels being built by Carpenters Unlimited were received on June 15. Our electrician has wired up two of them, and they have been installed on the left-hand wall of the trailer. This component of the project is on schedule.

2.3 Instructor's Console. Snags have again interrupted construction. Frank Dartmouth, in custom manufacturing, has identified the main problem as late delivery of modules from Capricorn Electronics in Vancouver, which has set his assembly schedule back by 15 work-days. He now predicts a completion date of August 19.

2.4 Display Booths. The two booths for displaying Vancourt equipment are complete and ready for installation in July. Marketing has assembled and tested the display equipment, and I have arranged for the two systems to be installed during the first two weeks of August.

2.5 Air Conditioning. The air conditioning unit was installed by the Kool-Air Company between June 12 and 16. Initial use of the air conditioner has identified two unsatisfactory conditions.

a) Moisture is running back into the trailer and dripping onto one of the newly installed carrels.

(8)

b) There is severe vibration and noise from the air conditioner.

(9)

The installation contractor has examined the air conditioner and will return on July 5 to correct these conditions.

(10) This is the **Problems** subcompartment. In paragraph 3.1 Roger forewarns management of a situation which may develop into a serious problem. He must comment on it again in next month's report, as he has done in paragraph 3.2 for the previous month's problem.

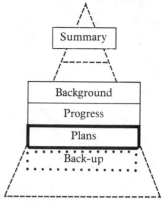

Normally, a previous month's problems are discussed *before* new problems are introduced (i.e. the continuing short-circuit problem in paragraph 3.2 should be mentioned before the new noise problem in paragraph 3.1). Roger has chosen to discuss the noise problem first because he wants to maintain continuity from the description of the unsatisfactory condition in the previous paragraph (paragraph 2.5).

(11) Roger combines the **Schedule** subcompartment and **Plans** compartment under one heading because the two topics are interrelated. Note how his closing statements in paragraphs 2.3 and 2.4 prepare readers for the changes in plans he announces in paragraph 4.1.

(12) The attachment mentioned here forms the **Back-up** compartment. (It has been omitted from the report to conserve space).

The guidelines on pages 43 to 45 provide only a basic framework for designing periodic progress reports. This framework can be adapted and shaped to suit individual requirements—just as Roger Korolick has adapted it—until the most efficient method is found for reporting progress.

Short Investigation Reports

Most investigation reports are longer reports which examine a problem or situation, identify its cause, suggest corrective measures or ways to improve the situation, evaluate the feasibility of each, and select which is most suitable. These are discussed in chapter 6. There are occasions, however, when only a minor or local problem is examined, and only a short, informal investigation report is needed to describe it. Such reports are described here.

2

(10) **3. Problems Encountered**

     3.1 I am concerned that the air conditioning unit will create a noise problem which will be unacceptable for the type of training we are planning. Already, installation personnel working in the trailer have commented that the noise is unusually high. Although the contractor has assured me that the noise level will drop significantly when the vibration problem is corrected and the carrels, booths, and carpet are installed, I doubt that the drop will be sufficient. We may have to find a means for further lessening the noise.

     3.2 The intermittent short-circuit condition in the trailer strip lighting, described in para 3.3 of my May report, was traced to a faulty switch and corrected on June 6.

(11) **4. Scheduling**

     4.1 To overcome the problem created by late delivery of the instructor's console, I am planning to advance the installation of the display booths by three weeks (to start on August 1), and to delay installation of the instructor's console until August 22. These changes are shown on the revised work plan attached to (12) this report.

     4.2 I expect the project to be completed by September 15, as scheduled.

R. Korolick

Roger Korolick
Project Coordinator
July 2, 19xx

The short investigation report has the four basic compartments described in chapter 2, plus the optional **Back-up** compartment. These compartments are illustrated in Figure 4-3 and outlined in more detail below.

- A **Summary Statement** briefly identifies the problem and how it was or can be resolved.

- A **Background** compartment outlines what caused an investigation to be carried out.

- The **Investigation** compartment describes the steps taken to establish the cause of the problem and find a remedy.

- The **Outcome** compartment describes what has been done to resolve the problem or, if other people have to take the necessary action, recommends what should be done.

- The optional **Back-up** compartment stores detailed supporting data evolving from the previous three compartments.

Very short investigation reports are usually issued as interoffice memorandums, or occasionally as letters. An example is printed on page 52.

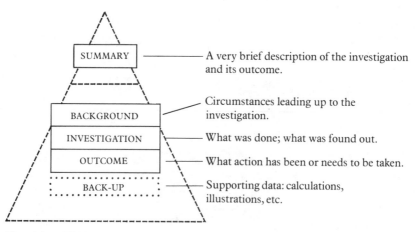

Fig. 4-3. *Writing compartments for a short investigation report.*

Short Investigation Report
Correcting an Electrical Problem

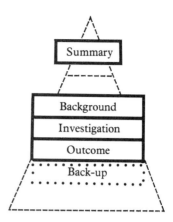

Comments

In the uncluttered one-page report on page 52, Tom Westholm places his information confidently into the report writing pyramid's five compartments.

(1) Although the subject line is vague, the word "correcting" serves a useful purpose because it implies that Tom has found a solution to the problem.

(2) Tom's **Summary Statement** identifies the problem, states its cause, reports that it has been resolved, and suggests what else should be done.

(3) The **Background** compartment describes events leading up to the investigation.

(4) In his **Investigation** compartment, Tom describes his approach to the problem and what he has discovered.

(5) The **Outcome** compartment describes not only how he corrected the problem, but also suggests a better alternative.

(6) Here, Tom refers to his **Back-up** information (which, to conserve space, has been omitted).

(7) This final question is part of the **Outcome** compartment.

Compare Tom Westholm's short, informal investigation report with Tod Phillips' five-page semiformal report in chapter 6. Note how the five compartments used for the short report are expanded to develop more information for the longer report.

INTER-OFFICE MEMORANDUM

To: C. Meaghan, Plant Manager   Date: July 9, 19xx

From: Tom Westholm   Ref: Correcting Electrical   (1)
       Maintenance Electrician   Blackouts

(2) I have traced the recent electrical power failures to a wiring
     error which created a power overload. Although I have corrected
     the problem, a better solution would be to install a separate
     power panel for two of the air conditioners.

(3) The failures started after the air conditioners were overhauled
     in May, and even then they occurred only infrequently and at
     random intervals. On every occasion simply resetting the circuit
     breakers corrected the failure, which made the cause difficult
     to identify.

(4) As I suspected the air conditioners, I compared the wiring connec-
     tions against the manufacturer's wiring diagrams but could find
     no fault. I then examined the four air conditioners in turn, and
     identified a disconnected load splitter behind air conditioner
     No. 2. The load splitter was installed six years ago, to prevent
     the circuit from being overloaded should more than two air con-
     ditioner compressors cut in at the same time. Apparently the over-
     haul contractor failed to reintroduce it into the circuit when
     re-installing the air conditioners in May.

(5) I have reconnected the load splitter, but suggest we could obtain
     better performance from the air conditioners if we were to install
     a new power control box and connect two of the air conditioners
     to it. We could then remove the load splitter. The cost would
(6) be $645.00, as detailed on the attached cost estimate.

(7) May I have your approval to buy the necessary parts and do the
     installation?

                              Tom.

PART THREE

Semiformal Reports and Proposals

5

Test and Laboratory Reports

Considerable variation exists in the presentation of test and laboratory reports (often called lab reports). Some laboratory reports simply describe the tests performed and the results obtained, and comment briefly on what the results mean. Others are much more comprehensive: they open with a synopsis of the tests and results; they continue by presenting full details of the background, purpose, equipment, methods, and results; and they finish with an analysis from which their authors draw conclusions. The more comprehensive laboratory report is described here, because the shorter, simpler form can be adapted from it.

A third form of laboratory report is used in universities and colleges, where students are asked to perform tests and then write a lab report to describe their findings. Comments on laboratory reports written in an academic environment start on page 65.

Industrial Laboratory Reports

Industrial laboratory reports are based on the report writers' pyramid described in chapter 2, but the **Facts** compartment is expanded to encompass the following four subcompartments:

1. Equipment & Materials.
2. Test Method.
3. Test Results.
4. Analysis.

There is also a **Back-up** compartment for holding specifications, procedures, and details of test measurements the author refers to. The major compartments and subcompartments are illustrated in Figure 5-1, and described in more detail on the pages facing the sample test report which starts on page 56.

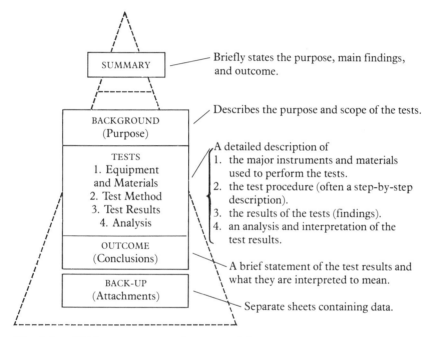

Fig. 5-1. *Writing compartments for a test or laboratory report.*

Industrial Laboratory Report
Testing a Water Stage Manometer

Comments

(1) Some organizations use a prepared form for the first page of their laboratory reports. The form has spaces for entering predetermined information, such as:

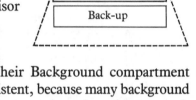

- Title and purpose of test.
- Name of client.
- Authority for test (i.e. purchase order, letter, etc).
- Summary of test results.
- Signature and typed name of person performing test.
- Signature of manager or supervisor approving test results.
- Date tests were completed.

Report authors using a form find their Background compartment becomes much shorter, or even nonexistent, because many background details are entered in the prepared spaces and need not be repeated.

(2) The **Summary** establishes what test was undertaken, sometimes why it was necessary, the main finding(s), and the result.

(3) The **Background** compartment starts here. Carole Winterton (the laboratory technician who performed the tests and wrote the report) has chosen to divide the compartment into two parts, each with its own heading: *History* and *Purpose of Test.*

(4) This is the start of both the large **Tests** compartment and the **Equipment and Materials** subcompartment.

The amount of information provided in the **Equipment and Materials** subcompartment depends on several factors. If the client may want to duplicate the tests or know more about how they were undertaken, or if the person performing the tests needs to demonstrate the extent of testing, a full description is provided; but if the client is more interested in results, and is not likely to be concerned with how the tests were run, then only essential details are included. (The same guideline applies to the Method subcompartment.)

If the equipment set-up and list of materials are complex or lengthy, they can be placed in an attachment.

ENVIRONMENTAL TEST LABS LIMITED

①   Test Report No. 34/07
June 14, 19xx

②   Summary of Test Results

Pressure tests of a Caledonia Water Stage Manometer model WSM, serial No. 2306, show that although all components are operating satisfactorily the manometer apparently has a minute, unidentifiable gas leak.

③   History

The manometer was shipped to the Test Lab from site 24 of the Agassiz Water Control System (AWCS). It was removed from service on May 22, following a visiting technician's report that the manometer was recording erratic, sharp changes in water stage which contradicted his visual observations of water levels. No tests of the manometer, or of the gas delivery system between it and the underwater orifice, could be performed in site because of the remoteness of the site.

Purpose of Test

In AWCS memorandum 0693 dated June 5, 19xx, we were requested to test the manometer, determine whether the manometer or the site's buried gas delivery system is causing the problem, and, if the manometer proves faulty, identify the cause.

④   Equipment Set-up

The manometer was installed on a workbench, levelled 18° from the vertical, and connected to a mock-up of the site's gas delivery system, which consisted of:

     a)   A cylinder of super-dry nitrogen, through a gas flow regulator.

     b)   30 metres of 5 mm ID polyethylene tubing terminating in a water tank, with the tube's orifice submerged 0.96 metre below the surface (to simulate site conditions).

     c)   A Franck and Corwin type B-37 continuous recorder.

The manufacturer's operating manual, publication 6425, was used as a reference. The test hook-up is shown in figure 1.

1

(5) A simple diagram showing how the test equipment is connected can help a reader visualize the test set-up. If the illustration of a test set-up is too large to fit on a standard page, it can be placed at the back of the report, labelled as an attachment, and referred to at the appropriate places within the report.

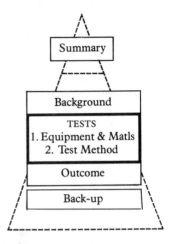

If several tests are performed, each with a varying arrangement of test equipment, it is better to insert a series of diagrams in the report, each positioned immediately ahead of or beside the appropriate test description.

(6) The **Method** subcompartment describes how the tests were carried out. It can range from a brief outline of the test method used (for a nontechnical reader interested primarily in results) to a step-by-step description of the procedure (for a reader who wants to know how comprehensive the test was). Carole has used a fairly detailed step-by-step description for her report, because her analysis of the results will depend on the reader fully understanding what was done during the tests.

(7) This initial paragraph is an internal summary statement used to introduce a lengthy segment of the report. Preparing readers to expect a certain arrangement of information helps them accept more readily the facts a report writer presents. By numbering and naming the three tests, Carole is silently saying, "These are the tests you will read about next, and this is the sequence in which I will be presenting them to you." She must now take care to describe them in the same sequence.

(8) Each test is numbered and given a subheading similar to that used in the section summary statement (7).

(9) When a process or procedure is lengthy, or is not essential to a full understanding of the report, the steps may be printed in an attachment and simply referred to in the report. (See also comment No. 16.)

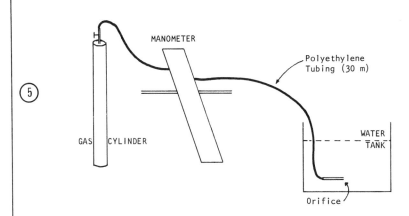

Fig. 1. Water Stage Manometer Test System

(5)

(6) Method

(7) Tests were made of 1) the nitrogen delivery system, 2) the manometer, and 3) the total system.

(8) 1. Tests of Nitrogen Gas Delivery System

The gas flow regulator of the nitrogen cylinder was first connected directly to the polyethylene tubing, the orifice in the water tank was temporarily plugged, and gas was allowed to flow into the system until the regulator gauge read 500 kPa. The tubing was then inspected for leaks; none were found and the pressure remained stable for the ensuing two hours of the test.

(9) The manometer was reconnected to the system and nitrogen was applied as specified in step 8 of the manufacturer's manual (see attachment 1). When a flow rate of 15 bubbles per minute had been achieved in the sight feed, the flow rate was checked at the orifice. It was a steady 8 bubbles per minute, which conforms to the manufacturer's specification of one-half the flow rate at the sight feed, plus or minus 15%.

The sight feed and orifice bubble rates were checked at two-hour intervals during the tests and remained within specification throughout.

2

(10) Carole has chosen to place these five steps within the report, rather than in an attachment, because she wants readers to be fully aware that steps (a) and (e) were performed *before* they read the test results and her analysis. They support her contention that the fault is unidentifiable and lies within the instrument she is testing.

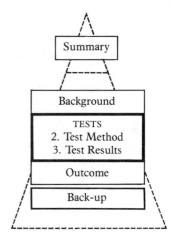

(11) The **Method** subcompartment of a report must be written in clear, direct language which is entirely objective (unbiased, without opinions).

(12) The pumping in and out of water has a direct bearing on, and is referenced in, the Results subcompartment. Consequently it must be described thoroughly here.

(13) The **Results** subcompartment describes the major finding evolving from the tests. Like the tests described in the Method subcompartment, the test results must be written objectively.

2. Check of Water Stage Manometer

   All external parts of the manometer were checked for proper operation.

   a) The bubble flow rate in the sight feed was observed at two-hour
      intervals during the system checks, and at 15-minute intervals
      during the final four hours. It remained constant and within
      specifications.

   b) The float switch contacts were examined and found to be clean.

   c) The set screw on the servo control was adjusted until the drive
      motor moved away from the correct setting. The servo control
      operated smoothly to follow the adjustment.

   d) The constant-differential pressure regulator was removed and cleaned.
      No foreign matter was found.

   e) A soapy solution was applied to all exposed connections, both on the
      manometer and to the gas delivery system. No bubbling occurred.

3. Check of Total System

   The system was allowed to stabilize for 3 hours, and then run continuously for 30 hours. For the first 26 hours the water in the tank was
   pumped in and out at controlled rates, to simulate changes in water stage.

   a) Water was pumped out at 10.75 litres per minute (L/min); after
      8 hours the head of water above the orifice had decreased from
      0.96 metre to 0.41 metre.

   b) Water was then pumped in at 11.4 L/min for 12 hours, after which
      the water head had increased to 1.32 metres.

   c) Water was again pumped out, this time at 8.4 L/min for 6 hours,
      until the water head had returned to 0.96 metre above the orifice.

   The system was run for a further 4 hours, with no change in water level,
   during which further manometer checks were performed. Throughout, the
   manometer appeared to operate correctly.

Test Results

Tests of the gas delivery system and of the water stage manometer showed no
apparent faults. But when the chart on the Franck and Corwin B-37 recorder
was removed and inspected at the end of the tests, it showed that a fault
existed somewhere in the system. Instead of recording a steady decrease,
increase, and then decrease of water head, the trace on the chart displayed
a series of "steps," indicated by apparent abrupt decreases of water level,
each followed by a slow recovery (see attachment 2). These "false troughs"
were present for increasing, decreasing, and stable water level conditions.

3

(14) In the **Analysis** subcompartment a report writer is expected to examine and interpret the test results, and to comment on their implications. The analysis should discuss various aspects influencing or evolving from the tests, and show how they lead to either a logical conclusion or an unanticipated outcome. This helps readers to understand and accept more readily the conclusions which follow.

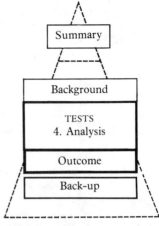

(15) This is the **Outcome** compartment. It should answer the question, resolve the problem, or respond to the request identified in the Background compartment (titled "Purpose of Test" in Carole's report). It must never introduce new data or present information which will surprise the reader.

(16) Attachments form the **Back-up** compartment. Their purpose is to provide a place for storing data which a reader does not need while reading the report but may want to inspect later. They may comprise a detailed procedure used during the tests, a lengthy table of test results containing measurements and dial readings, or photographs, sketches, and drawings.

All attachments must be referred to in the report (the attachment on page 64 is referred to here on the foot of page 2 of the report). They should be presented in the sequence in which they are mentioned in the report, and then numbered sequentially as "Attachment 1," "Attachment 2," etc.

Note: To conserve space in these guidelines, only attachment 1 is included with this report.

Analysis of Results

False troughs are caused by minute intermittent leaks in the total gas purge
system, resulting in a temporary loss of pressure. They appear on the chart
as a comparatively rapid drop in water level followed by a slow recovery,
usually of about one hour. Intermittent leaks are more likely to occur at
high water stages, with the result that crests are recorded one or two
metres below their true stage, although this was not apparent in our tests.
Very small intermittent leaks can be extremely difficult to locate.

We believe the leak is within the manometer, rather than in the gas delivery
system. The pre-test pressure check of the gas delivery system, and the
soap test of its connections, produced no evidence of leaks between the
manometer and the underwater orifice.

The erratic water level readings reported by the site and the false troughs
identified during the tests are probably different interpretations of an
identical fault. Since a different gas delivery system was used in each
case, the problem is more likely to be within the manometer.

Conclusions

Our tests show that the erratic water stage readings recorded at AWCS site
24 were probably caused by a tiny, undetectable internal gas leak in the
water stage manometer. The site's gas delivery system is less likely to
have caused the fault.

Tests performed by   Approved by

Carole Winterton   Frederick L. Cairns, P.Eng
Lab Technician III   Supervisor, Tests & Procedures

4

Attachment 1

EXTRACT FROM MANUFACTURER'S OPERATING MANUAL
FOR WATER STAGE MANOMETER MODEL WSM

8. Instructions for Purging the System

To purge (introduce nitrogen gas into) the system, proceed exactly
in the following sequence:

8.1 Check that the following valves are closed:

Valve	Rotation
Feed pressure adjustment screw	fully CCW
Feed rate adjustment needle valve	fully CW
Manometer shut-off valve	fully CW

8.2 Turn the bubble tube shut-off valve fully CW (open).

8.3 Turn the nitrogen cylinder valve fully CCW (open).

8.4 Rotate the feed pressure adjustment screw slowly CW until the
pressure gauge reads 280 kPa.

8.5 Rotate the feed rate adjustment valve slowly CCW until bubbles
can be seen flowing in the manometer sight feed. Adjust the
valve until the flow rate is 15 bubbles per minute.

8.6 Check that the flow rate at the orifice is 7 or 8 bubbles
per minute.

5

Academic Laboratory Reports

Laboratory reports written in an academic setting use the same writing compartments as those written in industry (see Figure 5-1), but there is a shift in purpose and emphasis. An industrial laboratory report responds to a specific request or demand, and so answers a question or meets a stated need. An academic laboratory report is used by students to prove a hypothesis or test a theory, or as a vehicle for helping them learn how to perform a particular test or understand a process or procedure. Normally it does not respond to a tangible demand (other than a professor's request) or meet a specific need. It may, however, answer a question.

   The science and engineering departments at each university or college also specify differing requirements for lab reports, which makes it difficult to specify exact writing compartments. Those described here offer the most generally accepted approach.

- A **Summary** which includes a brief statement of the purpose or objective of the tests, the major findings, and what was deduced from them.

- A more detailed statement of **Purpose** or **Objective**, plus other pertinent background data. (This writing compartment may be combined with the Summary if there is little background information.)

- An **Equipment Set-up** compartment, which provides a list of the equipment and materials used for the tests, and a description and illustration of how the equipment was interconnected. (If there is a series of tests requiring different equipment configurations, a full list of equipment and materials should appear here. A description and illustration of each set-up should then be inserted at the beginning of each test description.)

- A **Method** compartment, containing a step-by-step detailed description of each test, similar to the Test Method section of an industrial laboratory report. Attachments may be used for lengthy procedures or process information.

- A **Results** compartment, giving a statement of the test results, or findings evolving from the tests.

- A detailed **Analysis** of the results or findings, their implications, and what can be learned or interpreted from them.

- A **Conclusions** compartment, comprising a brief statement describing how the tests, findings, and resulting analysis have met the objective stated in the Objective or Purpose compartment.

- A **Data** (**Attachments**) compartment, which is placed on a separate sheet (or sheets). It contains data derived during the tests, such as detailed calculations, measurements, weights, stresses, and sound levels. Lengthy procedures or process descriptions are sometimes included as attachments.

If several tests were performed, and there were results from each, it may be better to have separate Equipment Set-up, Method and Results compartments for each test. The organization plan would then be:

Summary
Objective or Purpose
Equipment and Materials
Test No. 1:
    Equipment Set-up
    Method
    Results
Test No. 2:
    Equipment Set-up
    Method
    Results
Test No. 3:
    Equipment Set-up
    Method
    Results
Analysis
Conclusions
Data (Attachments)

6

Investigation and Evaluation Reports

An investigation report describes a problem or situation that has been investigated, examines methods for correcting the problem or improving the situation, and usually suggests what should be done. If the report evaluates alternatives (such as an examination of several sites for locating a fast-food restaurant), it may be called an evaluation report; if it examines the practicability of doing something new or different, it may be called a feasibility study.

Investigation reports can be as short as only one or two pages, but more often they are much longer, ranging from 3 to 30 or 40 pages. Shorter reports are normally typed as interoffice memorandums or letters, while longer reports may have a title centred at the head of the first page (which makes them eligible to be labelled "semiformal reports"). Some are even given the full formal report treatment shown in chapter 8.

A very short investigation report has five compartments, which are shown in Figure 4-3 on page 50. For longer investigation reports the compartments are expanded to introduce subcompartments as shown in Figure 6-1. These compartments and subcompartments are identified and described in greater depth in the comments for the five-page investigation report which starts on page 71.

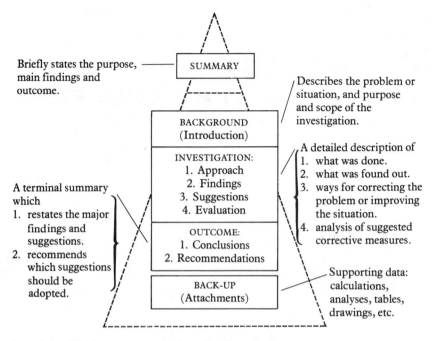

Briefly states the purpose, main findings and outcome.

Describes the problem or situation, and purpose and scope of the investigation.

A terminal summary which
1. restates the major findings and suggestions.
2. recommends which suggestions should be adopted.

A detailed description of
1. what was done.
2. what was found out.
3. ways for correcting the problem or improving the situation.
4. analysis of suggested corrective measures.

Supporting data: calculations, analyses, tables, drawings, etc.

SUMMARY

BACKGROUND (Introduction)

INVESTIGATION:
1. Approach
2. Findings
3. Suggestions
4. Evaluation

OUTCOME:
1. Conclusions
2. Recommendations

BACK-UP (Attachments)

Fig. 6-1. *Writing compartments for a long investigation report.*

Semiformal Investigation Report
Study of High Gas Consumption
(Pages 71 to 79)

Comments

Throughout his report author Tod Phillips keeps his readers firmly in mind. He is aware that although he has done his investigation and is preparing his report for the Marsland Construction Company, his real readers are the homeowners, Mr and Ms Parsenon. For their sake he develops his case carefully, and uses language and terminology which they will readily understand.

If the Marsland Construction Company had simply asked Tod to investigate the cause of high gas consumption, and if he knew that only the company would use the information, then he could be much more direct. He could tell them in one sentence that he has checked the gas furnace, hot air ducts, gas flow meter, and insulation, and found them all to be satisfactory. And then he could go straight into his comparative analysis of gas consumption records and thermostat settings. But Tod has been briefed by Marsland Construction Company that the report is needed specifically for the Parsenons, who have complained of high gas consumption ever since the house was new and they first occupied it. Over the years Marsland has done numerous checks, made many adjustments, and found little wrong with the house. And yet the Parsenons have still complained. Finally, Marsland called in a professional consultant (Tod Phillips of H L Winman and Associates) and asked him to carry out an independent study which would identify the cause of the problem and recommend how it could be resolved. Marsland could then present the results to the homeowners to persuade them that the construction company has done all it can to rectify the problem. As Jack Marsland told Tod Phillips during their initial discussion, "Whatever you discover that is wrong, we'll fix if it's our fault. Then I can use your report to get the Parsenons off my back!"

Tod Phillips has written a semiformal report, although its length is such that he could also have prepared it in letter form. Some comments on the implications of using either format, and of addressing the report directly to the homeowners rather than to the construction company, follow the report (on page 80).

The comments that follow are cross-referenced to the corresponding numbers marked beside the investigation report.

(1) A title or main heading should be noticeable and informative—it should describe what the report is about. Too often, a report title can leave readers wondering what the report covers; for example, "Gas Consumption Investigation Report" would have been an inadequate title in this situation.

(2) A **Summary** carries the report's highlights, stated as briefly as possible. For an investigation report the Summary should cover:

- the purpose of the investigation *("Our investigation of heating fuel consumption...")*,

- the major findings *("...consumption... only slightly higher than in comparable homes...")*, and

- the major conclusions and/or recommendations *("...consumption can be reduced...by maintaining a lower home temperature...and insulating...")*.

In a long report like this, the summary is often written *after* the rest of the report. The report writer can then extract the highlights from the Background, Facts & Events, and Outcome compartments.

(3) When headings are used in a report, the **Background** compartment is titled "Introduction." An Introduction usually contains three pieces of information, not necessarily in the following order:
1. The events leading up to the investigation.
2. The purpose of the investigation.
3. The scope of the investigation.

(4) The **Approach** subcompartment starts here by explaining that the study had two phases, and so prepares the reader to find these two phases treated separately. Indeed, the heading immediately following this paragraph tells the reader that phase one is about to start.

(5) Not all of the headings exactly parallel the compartments used to write the report. To place a heading at the beginning of each compartment would have made the report too rigidly structured. Tod Phillips used the compartments to ensure that he was organizing his report properly, and then later inserted headings where they would help readers see the logical divisions of information. Headings which most often parallel the report writing compartments include:

Summary (Main Message)
Introduction (Background)
Conclusions and Recommendations (Outcome)
Attachments (Back-up)

H. L. Winman and Associates

PROFESSIONAL CONSULTING ENGINEERS

---

①
       STUDY OF REPORTED HIGH GAS CONSUMPTION AT 1404 GREGORY AVENUE

Summary

②
Our investigation of heating fuel consumption in Mr and Ms R M Parsenon's bungalow at 1404 Gregory Avenue shows consumption to be 4.37% higher than in homes of comparable size and construction. We believe consumption can be reduced to a normal or even lower level by maintaining the home at a slightly lower temperature and by insulating the upper 1.25 metres of the basement walls. Even greater fuel savings could be achieved by installing additional insulation in the ceiling and walls.

Introduction

③
The investigation followed lengthy correspondence between Marsland Construction Company, who built the bungalow, and the homeowners, who have continually reported excessively high fuel consumption and uncomfortably cold floors. In a letter dated February 16, 19xx, Marsland Construction Company authorized us to carry out an independent study which would determine the extent of high fuel consumption, identify the cause, and suggest remedies.

④
We divided the study into two phases: a physical check of the building and its heating system, and a comparison of gas consumption in the Parsenon home with that of similar bungalows.

⑤
Checks of Building and Heating System

⑥
Our examination of the Parsenon residence involved checks of the gas furnace and hot air ducts, the gas company's flow meter, and the insulation.

⑦
The gas furnace and hot air ducts were examined by Montrose Heating and Supply Specialists Ltd. Both were found to be in good condition, with the exception of the humidifier plates in the furnace which were badly corroded. Their poor condition might cause slightly lower humidity in the home but would not affect the temperature. Low humidity, however, might create the impression of a lower-than-desirable temperature. New humidifier plates were installed, and a spare set was left with the homeowners for installation in one year's time.

1

(6)   This short paragraph continues the **Approach** subcompartment by identifying what physical checks will be carried out in the Parsenon home. An "overview" paragraph following a section heading is useful because it prepares the reader to expect a certain narrative sequence.

Later in the report—at (9)—a second Approach paragraph will describe how the comparative analysis was carried out. Although many investigation reports have a straight-through discussion, in which the *whole* approach is presented first and is followed immediately by *all* the findings, Tod has chosen to use a two-stage method because he has two distinctive aspects to deal with: the physical check of the home, and the comparative analysis of gas consumption records.

(7)   The **Findings** subcompartment starts here and continues through four paragraphs. [A second set of findings appears later in the report, at (11).]

(8)   Tod has found that the problem lies entirely with the homeowners, and not with the construction company. So he has to tell Mr and Ms Parsenon something they don't really want to hear— that the builder is blameless and that they have to take whatever corrective action is necessary. Consequently he has to *persuade* them to accept his findings.

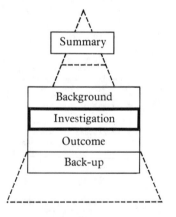

His careful accumulation of *evidence* in this first set of investigation findings does exactly that. He cannot dismiss the insulation and heating equipment in just a few words, because the Parsenons most likely suspect that these are the cause of their problem. So he carefully examines each aspect, quotes *facts* to prove there are no faults, and in no case allows his personal opinions to intrude. By the end of this section there must be no doubt in the Parsenons' minds that the fault lies elsewhere.

(9)   This is the second part of the **Approach** subcompartment.

(10) A reader should be able to read a whole report right through without having to turn to the attachments, but should always be informed at appropriate places that supportive evidence is attached, and where to find it.

We asked Montrose Gas Company to check the gas flow meter. They reported that it had been replaced twice in the past twelve months at the house-holders' request, and on both occasions no fault could be found. Neither could they find fault with the present flow meter.

We checked the bungalow's insulation and found:

(8)

    a) The ceiling has a minimum of 180 millimetres of wood chips, which is equivalent to an R16 insulation factor.

    b) The walls have Fibreglass insulation with an R8 insulation factor.

    c) The basement is unfinished and uninsulated.

Although this level of insulation would not meet government standards for a dwelling built today (i.e. R40 in the ceiling and R20 in the walls), it fully meets the insulation requirements which were in effect when the home was built in 1975.

(9) Comparison with Comparable Homes

As our checks of the Parsenon dwelling showed no significant cause for the reported high gas consumption, we decided to compare consumption in Mr and Ms Parsenon's home with that of two groups of bungalows of comparable age and size. They comprised:

    Four identical homes built by the same contractor. They were Gregory Avenue numbers 1396, 1399, 1407, and 1410.

    Four homes built at the same time, but by other contractors. They were Gregory Avenue numbers 1506, 1515, 1524, and 1581.

In each case we obtained permission from the homeowners to quote their con-sumption records for the calendar year 19xx. We also asked homeowners to inform us if any additional insulation had been installed since their bungalows were built, and the setting at which they kept their thermostats.

(10) The results are shown in the attached table.

Examination of the comparison table shows that:

(11)

    1. Gas consumption in the Parsenon home for 19xx was 38 MCF (38 000 cubic feet), or 4.37% greater than the average of the eight other homes we evaluated.

    2. The thermostat in the Parsenon home was set $1.3^{\circ}C$ higher by day, and $3.8^{\circ}C$ higher at night, than the average setting for the eight other homes.

2

(11) The second set of investigation findings starts here. The results of this part of the investigation are based on evidence supplied in an attached comparative analysis. Tod presents his findings here without discussion; in effect he is saying to readers, "This is what I found out, and you can verify all of it by referring to the comparative analysis." His use of brief subparagraphs (point form) helps maintain a detached, almost clinical, presentation of these facts.

(12) In the **Suggestions** subcompartment a report writer can offer a single suggestion, several suggestions, or alternative suggestions. Tod presents two main suggestions, and implies that one should be adopted while the other is optional.

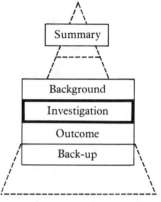

(13) The **Evaluation** subcompartment allows a report writer to shed some of his or her impartiality. Readers like to form their own opinions of the validity of each suggestion, but need a convincing, logical, rational evaluation on which to base them. They depend on the report writer to evaluate factors such as:

• feasibility,
• suitability,
• simplicity,
• effectiveness, and
• cost.

(Sometimes a report writer may also have to evaluate the effect of taking *no* action; i.e. adopting none of the suggestions.)

Tod Phillips has to convince his secondary readers (the homeowners, Mr and Ms Parsenon) that they must take at least one step, and preferably two, to resolve their problem. He tries to persuade them to accept his suggestions by:

• Mustering evidence to show they have to lower the temperature in their bungalow. (He quotes federal specifications to demonstrate what gas saving they should be able to achieve, and then reinforces his case by referring to local residents who are achieving such savings.)

3. Gas consumption for the six homes in which the thermostat setting was lowered at night was consistently lower than the comsumption in the three homes in which the thermostat setting was not lowered.

4. Gas consumption in Marsland-built homes was comparable to that in homes built by other contractors.

5. Two homes in which some additional insulation has been installed consumed significantly less gas than homes which have only their original insulation.

Methods for Reducing Gas Consumption

We believe Mr and Ms Parsenon can reduce gas consumption in their home to an average level, or even slightly better than average, at little or no cost. This reduction can be achieved by lowering the thermostat setting from its present constant 22.5°C to 21° during the day and 18° at night. They could also achieve a further significant reduction, but at extra cost, by installing additional insulation in the ceiling, walls, and basement.

Although it is difficult to predict an exact saving in gas consumption, Federal Insulation Specification FIS-2820/78 suggests that for every 1000 cubic feet of floor space, each half-degree (Celsius) reduction in house temperature conserves about 10.3 MCF of gas annually (MCF = 1000 cubic feet). In Mr and Ms Parsenon's residence, a 1.5°C reduction in temperature should therefore cut consumption by 30.9 MCF annually. We also believe that a further 8 to 10 MCF of gas could be saved annually by reducing the temperature to 18°C at night. These estimates seem to be borne out by the consumption figures for the homes at 1407, 1506, and 1581 Gregory Avenue, in which lower temperatures are maintained without additional house insulation.

Ms Parsenon has commented that they are forced to keep their home temperature at 22.5° because at any lower temperature the floor is unbearably cold. We asked the owners of an identical bungalow at 1410 Gregory Avenue, who maintain a 20.5° temperature in their home, if their floors are similarly cold. Their experience offers a probable solution. After the basement of their bungalow was insulated, they found the floors to be considerably warmer, and that they could reduce the temperature from its previous 22° to 20.5° without discomfort.

The basement at 1410 Gregory Avenue has been fully insulated. We believe it would be necessary to insulate only the upper 1.25 metres of a basement to obtain a similar result, because below the 1.25 metre level the walls are insulated naturally by the surrounding soil. Basement insulation is easily applied by nailing or gluing styrofoam panels directly onto the walls. We estimate that to insulate the upper 4 metres of the basement in the Parsenon residence would cost $450 if the work is done by a contractor, or $180 if it is done by the homeowners.

3

- Suggesting they would be wise to insulate at least part of their basement. (He acknowledges their problem of cold floors, and then
  points to what someone else has done.)
- Explaining how they could gain additional savings by installing more
  insulation in the walls and ceiling of their home. (He recognizes
  this would be costly, and so presents it only as an option.)

It would be difficult to refute the validity of Tod's evaluation. It is
carefully developed, so that it carries readers logically from one point
to the next. By now, Tod's readers should feel they *know* what the
conclusions and recommendations are going to be.

(14) Tod has written a straightforward evaluation because he is offering
several suggestions which will have a cumulative effect. His readers
have to decide how many of his suggestions should be adopted, rather
than choose between them. He might have arranged his information
differently if there had been alternative suggestions.

For example, suppose that you have
investigated several word processing
systems to identify which would be most
suitable to install in your office. Now
you have to write an investigation report
to management, in which you will
recommend the best system. There are
two methods you can use for arranging
the **Suggestions** and **Evaluation**
subcompartments:

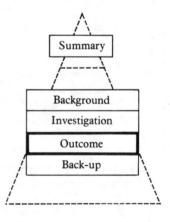

- You can present all the suggestions
  first, and then evaluate them (as Tod
  has done).

      Suggestions:
      System A
      System B
      System C

  Evaluation:
      System A
      System B
      System C

Installing additional insulation in the ceiling and walls of the Parsenon home would achieve even greater savings in gas consumption, and also enhance the comfort level at the suggested thermostat settings. In 19xx, the fully insulated home at 1515 Gregory Avenue consumed 55.1 MCF less gas than the average for the eight homes we evaluated, and 93.1 MCF less gas than Mr and Ms Parsenon's bungalow. Significantly, it is also the largest bungalow in the group.

Because the cost of insulating the ceiling and walls, and even the basement, of their home will depend on the quality (R factor) of insulation they desire, we suggest that if Mr and Ms Parsenon want to install additional insulation they should obtain the advice of, and an estimate from, a recognized insulation contractor.

Conclusions

Our study shows that gas consumption in Mr and Ms Parsenon's home is 4.37% higher than average, and that this high consumption is caused primarily by the dwelling being maintained at higher-than-average room temperature.

Consumption could be reduced to average for this type and size of dwelling by lowering the thermostat level 1½°C by day, and 5°C at night, and by maintaining an optimum humidity level. It could be reduced to better than average by also installing additional insulation.

Recommendations

We recommend that Mr and Ms Parsenon reduce the temperature in their home to 21°C during the day, and 18°C at night, increase the floor temperature by insulating the upper 1.25 metres of the basement walls, and maintain constant humidity by replacing the humidifier plates in the gas furnace at least once a year.

If this does not achieve the desired reduction in gas consumption, then we suggest that Mr and Ms Parsenon install additional insulation in the walls and ceiling of their home.

J E Phillips

Tod E Phillips
March 16, 19xx

4

- You can present each suggestion in turn, and then immediately evaluate it.

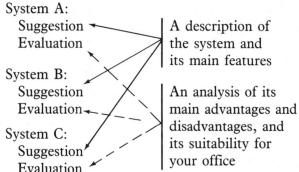

(15) The conclusions and recommendations form the report's **Outcome** compartment. They present the results of the investigation, suggest what needs to be done, and sometimes recommend what action the reader should take.

The conclusions should repeat the main features of the **Findings** subcompartment. They must never introduce any information or ideas which have not been discussed previously in the report.

(16) Recommendations must be strong and definite. They should be stated in the active voice, rather than in the bland passive voice. That is, they should say "I recommend…" or "We recommend…", and *not* "It is recommended that…". And they should never recommend action which has not already been discussed in the report.

(17) The signature at the end of the report is optional. But the date the report is issued should be included, either here or immediately after the report title.

(18) Attachments (sometimes called Appendices) hold factual evidence which supports statements made in the report, but which is too comprehensive, complex, or detailed to be included with the main narrative. They may be calculations, analyses, cost estimates, drawings, photographs, plans, or copies of other documents. They form the **Back-up** compartment of the report writing pyramid.

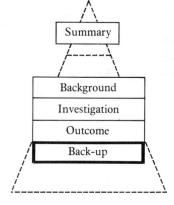

⑱

<u>ATTACHMENT</u>

COMPARISON OF GAS CONSUMPTION

IN NINE GREGORY AVENUE BUNGALOWS

FOR CALENDAR YEAR 19XX

House No.	Year Built	Size (sq ft)	Consumption (in MCF)*	Thermostat Setting (Day °C)	(Night °C)	Additional Insulation
R M Parsenon Residence						
1404	1975	1004	906.4	22.5	22.5	None
Identical Homes Built by Marsland Construction Company						
1396	1975	1004	870.6	22.0	18.0	None
1399	1974	1004	894.4	21.0	21.0	None
1407	1974	1004	880.9	21.0	17.5	None
1410	1975	1004	841.3	20.5	20.5	Basement
Group Average:		1004	871.8	21.1	19.2	
Nonidentical Homes Built by Other Contractors						
1506	1973	966	868.9	21.5	16.5	None
1515	1976	1080	813.3	21.0	16.5	Ceiling, Walls Basement
1524	1973	980	900.3	22.0	22.0	None
1581	1973	966	877.5	21.0	18.0	None
Group Average:		998	865.0	21.4	18.2	
AVERAGE OF 8 CONTROL HOMES:		1001	868.4	21.2	18.7 ′	

* MCF = 1000 cubic feet

5

Certain "rules" apply to attachments.

- Readers should not have to turn back to them as they read the report (although they may choose to refer to them later). This means that the most significant features of an attachment must be quoted in the investigation narrative.
- Every attachment must be referred to in the report narrative. It must serve a specific purpose, and never be included simply because it contains possibly useful information.
- The attachments should appear in the order in which they are referred to in the narrative. If there is more than one attachment, they should be numbered Attachment 1, Attachment 2, etc. (Or, if they are referred to as appendices, as Appendix A, B, C, etc.)

Comparison Between Semiformal and Letter-Form Investigation Reports

A semiformal investigation report is generally longer, seems to have more dignity, and appears to be more formal than a letter. Its title is centred at the top, its contents are clearly divided into compartments each preceded by a heading, and its language is usually a little less personal. It can be a useful way to convey information when the contents of a report are meant to influence a third party. (In the example, the report is written for the Marsland Construction Company but its results are really intended for the homeowners.)

Because it is not addressed to a particular reader, a semiformal investigation report often needs to be accompanied by a cover letter. The cover letter serves two purposes:

- It very briefly summarizes the results presented in the report.
- It provides a place for report writers to make comments they might prefer not to insert in the report.

The cover letter that accompanied Tod Phillips' report for the Marsland Construction Company does both:

Dear Mr Marsland:

Our investigation at 1404 Gregory Avenue shows that Mr and Ms Parsenon's complaint of high gas consumption is partly justified. We find, however, that it is caused by the high temperature at which they keep their home rather than by faulty heating equipment or inadequate insulation.

We hope the attached report will help you convince Mr and

Ms Parsenon to take the appropriate steps necessary to bring gas consumption down to an acceptable level.

Sincerely

Tod Phillips

A letter-form investigation report, however, does not normally exceed three or four pages, addresses the recipient personally, and may still contain headings. If Tod Phillips's report had been written *as a letter* to the Marsland Construction Company, the first paragraph (the Summary) probably would not have changed. However, subsequent paragraphs would have contained more personal pronouns, such as "you," "your," "we," and "our." For example, the second paragraph—at (3)—probably would have looked like this:

> Our investigation followed your lengthy correspondence with Mr and Ms Parsenon regarding their complaints of high gas consumption and cold floors. In your letter of February 16, 19xx, you authorized us to determine the extent of high fuel consumption, identify the cause, and suggest possible remedies.

This "personalization" of a report's language becomes even more noticeable when the person to whom a letter report is addressed is an individual citizen rather than a company. If Tod Phillips had addressed his report directly to Mr and Ms Parsenon, rather than to the construction company, even its summary would have been more personal:

> Dear Mr and Ms Parsenon:
> We have investigated the reported high heating fuel consumption in your home, and have found it to be 4.37% higher than in homes of comparable age, size, and construction. Our checks revealed neither faults in the heating system, nor inadequate insulation of your bungalow during construction. Comparison with comparable homes, however, showed that the high gas consumption is probably caused by the higher-than-average temperature at which you maintain your home.
> We believe you could reduce gas consumption to a normal or even lower level by maintaining a slightly lower temperature in your bungalow during the day, lowering the thermostat to about 18°C at night, and insulating the upper 1.25 metres of the basement walls. If you want to obtain even greater fuel savings, then we suggest you consider installing additional insulation in the ceiling and walls.
> Our investigation was requested by...(etc)

7

Suggestions
and Proposals

Proposals vary from short memorandums to multi-volume hardbound documents. Those discussed here are the shorter, less formal versions which an individual is more likely to write, ranging from a single page to probably five or six pages.

There are three types of proposals:

- Informal suggestions.
- Semiformal proposals.
- Formal proposals.

A **Suggestion** offers an idea and briefly discusses its advantages and disadvantages. (For example, a supervisor may suggest to a department manager that break times be staggered, to avoid line-ups at the mobile refreshment wagon.) Most suggestions are internal documents and are written as memorandums.

A **Semiformal Proposal** presents ideas for resolving a problem or improving a situation, evaluates them against certain criteria, and often recommends what action should be taken. (For example, a supervisor may propose to management that steps be taken to overcome production bottlenecks in the company's packing department. He or she might suggest introducing new packaging equipment, discuss various alternatives such as hiring additional staff or embarking on a training programme, and then recommend the most suitable approach.) A semiformal proposal may be written as a memorandum or letter, or even in semiformal report format.

A **Formal Proposal** describes an organization's plans for carrying out a large project for a major client or the government. It is a substantial, often impressive document which describes in considerable detail what will be done, how and when it will be done, why the organization has the capability to do the work, and what it will cost. Such proposals are often prepared in response to a "Request for Proposal" (RFP), and are almost always submitted as bound books similar to a formal report. In extreme cases they may run to several volumes.

Writing compartments are illustrated and described for all three types of proposals, and examples (with accompanying comments) are provided for the informal suggestion (page 85) and semiformal proposal (page 89).

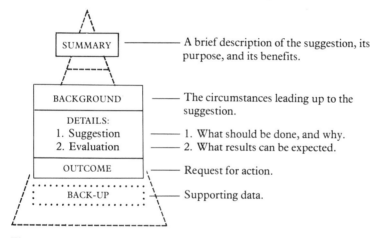

Fig. 7-1. *Writing compartments for an informal suggestion.*

Informal Suggestions

The writing compartments for an informal suggestion are illustrated in Figure 7-1.

* The **Summary** states very briefly what the proposer wants to do or wants done.
* The **Background** compartment describes the present situation.
* The **Details** compartment has two components:
  1. A **Suggestion** section, which outlines the suggested changes or improvements, and describes why they are needed.

2. An **Evaluation** section, which identifies what effect the suggested changes or improvements will have, and categorizes them into advantages and disadvantages (sometimes called "Gains" and "Losses").

- The **Outcome** compartment identifies what action needs to be taken. It can either request approval for the author to implement his or her suggestion, or identify who should take the necessary action, and possibly describe when and how it should occur.

- An optional **Back-up** compartment contains supporting data such as cost estimates, records, plans, and sketches.

Informal Suggestion
Proposal for a Study
Comments

When an informal suggestion is as short as Anne Martin's (opposite), the writing compartments may not be as clearly evident as those used to shape a longer memo, letter, or report. Nevertheless they are still there, contributing to the overall organization of her suggestion.

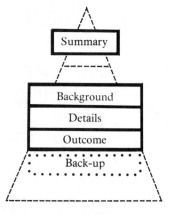

(1) Anne uses a cause-and-effect approach for her **Summary Statement**, first very briefly identifying her reason, and then stating what she would like to do in general terms.

(2) This paragraph is the **Background** compartment; it amplifies the reason stated in the Summary.

(3) The **Details** paragraph contains a specific **Suggestion**, in sentence 1, and a short **Evaluation**, which spells out what is to be gained (sentence 2) and the cost (sentence 3). Anne keeps the evaluation short by referring to details in an attachment (i.e. in the **Back-up** data). To conserve space the attachment is not included here.

(4) In the **Outcome** compartment Anne states specifically what she wants to do, and requests approval (action).

```
              THE WESTERN FARM IMPLEMENT COMPANY

                   Inter-office  Memorandum

   From:  Anne Martin, Accountant          Date:  October 13, 19xx

   To:    Frank Kelvin, President          Subject:  Proposal for Computer Study
```

(1) Now that our business volume has reached a level where we probably should be employing a computer for accounting and inventory control, I propose we engage a consultant to identify our exact needs.

(2) Presentations made to me over the past 12 months by representatives of several computer companies have almost convinced me that we need a computer, but which system will best meet our current and future needs neither I nor anyone else in the company is qualified to evaluate.

(3) I would like to obtain an objective analysis from Brian Lundeen of Antioch Business Consultants. As his attached letter describes, he will assess our existing and potential business volume and, if he believes we need a computer, will evaluate alternatives and recommend the best system. He has quoted a firm price of $850.00 to undertake such a study.

(4) I suggest we authorize Antioch Business Systems to carry out the study, and request your approval to go ahead.

                                              Anne

Semiformal Proposals

A semiformal proposal is more comprehensive than an informal suggestion, in the following ways:

- It usually deals with more complex situations, such as a problem or unsatisfactory condition.
- It discusses the circumstances in more detail.
- It establishes criteria (guidelines) for any proposed changes.

- It frequently offers alternatives, rather than a single suggestion.
- It analyzes the proposed alternatives in depth.
- It has a more formal appearance.

The writing compartments for a semiformal proposal are shown in Figure 7-2.

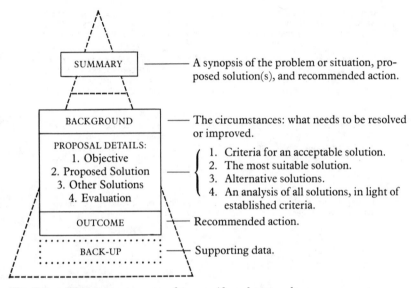

Fig. 7-2.   *Writing compartments for a semiformal proposal.*

- The **Summary** briefly describes the main highlights of the proposal, drawn mostly from the Background, Solutions, and Outcome compartments. If headings are used in the proposal, this compartment is preceded by the word SUMMARY or ABSTRACT.
- The **Background** compartment introduces the problem, situation, or unsatisfactory condition, and outlines the circumstances leading up to it. It may be preceded by the heading INTRODUCTION.

- The **Objective** subcompartment defines what needs to be achieved to resolve the problem, and establishes criteria for an optimum, or best, solution. This information may be included as part of the INTRODUCTION or preceded by a heading of its own (such as REQUIREMENTS or CRITERIA).
- The two **Solutions** subcompartments describe various ways the problem can be resolved or the situation improved. Each alternative should include:
  1. a description of the solution,
  2. the result or improvement it would achieve,
  3. how it would be implemented,
  4. its advantages and disadvantages, and
  5. its cost.
  Ideally, the alternative solutions will be arranged in descending order of suitability. These two subcompartments may be preceded by a single heading, such as METHODS FOR INCREASING PRODUCTIVITY, or by several descriptive headings.
- The **Evaluation** subcompartment analyzes and compares the alternative solutions, with particular reference to the criteria established in the Objective subcompartment. It may briefly discuss the effects of:
  1. adopting the proposed solution,
  2. adopting each of the alternative solutions, and
  3. adopting none of the solutions (i.e. taking no action).
- The **Outcome** compartment recommends what action should be taken. It should be worded using strong, positive terms and, if headings are used, the section should be preceded by the single word RECOMMENDATION.
- The **Back-up** compartment, if used, contains detailed analyses, test results, drawings, etc, which support and amplify statements made in the previous compartments. It is usually preceded by the heading ATTACHMENTS or APPENDICES.

The semiformal proposal on the following pages shows how these compartments can help organize information into a coherent, convincing, persuasive document.

Analysis of a Semiformal Proposal
"Evaluation of Photocopiers"

The notes below offer comments on Lorraine Dychuk's semiformal proposal on the facing pages.

Comments

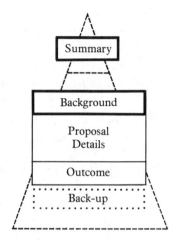

(1) The proposal's title is important: it should entice readers' interest. The key word here is "Improved."

(2) In a proposal the **Summary** should clearly identify:

- the purpose (why a change is necessary).
- the proposal (what the change involves), and
- the result (what is to be gained).

These should be highlights drawn from the Background, Proposal Details, and Outcome compartments. The SUMMARY heading is optional.

(3) A **Summary** should encourage readers to read further, preferably by making the major gain(s) or advantage(s) readily apparent. A demonstrated cost saving always appeals to management.

(4) The longer a proposal, the more need there is for headings. Those Lorraine uses help her readers "see" her organization plan as they read. A list of the primary headings shows the logical sequence of her report.

Heading	*Writing Compartment*
Summary	— **Summary**
Existing Photocopier Facilities	— **Background**
Proposed Photocopier System Other Systems and Configurations Evaluation of Alternatives	— **Proposal Details**
Conclusions Recommendations	— **Outcome**
Attachments	— **Back-up**

(5) The **Background** compartment starts here.

(6) Rather than introduce a detailed cost analysis into the proposal narrative, it's better to place the details in an attachment (to become

---

①   PROPOSAL FOR IMPROVED COPYING FACILITIES

by

Lorraine Dychuk
Systems Analyst

② <u>Summary</u>

My evaluation of the company's existing photocopiers shows that by adopting
an alternative system we could obtain better photocopying services at lower
cost. To achieve this objective I propose that the company consolidate its
copying services to a central location and exchange the four middle-range
copiers we now use for one top-flight copier with much greater capabilities.
③ The cost saving will be a minimum $122 per month, or 11.5% less than our
current copying costs.

④ <u>Existing Photocopier Facilities</u>

⑤ The company has four photocopiers, each used in a different location. They
are:

* Two leased Valiant "Fascopy" machines, one in the front office and
  one in the Production department.

* A leased Vancourt "PRO MK 1," which is shared by the Marketing and
  Information Systems departments.

* A company-owned Aetna "Little Gem," in the Purchasing and Supply
  department.

The three leased machines together cost $460 per month for their basic
leases, plus an additional charge for each copy made. These "per copy"
charges, when combined with the cost of materials such as paper and printing
fluids, amount to a further $596 per month, for an average total monthly
⑥ cost of $1056. A breakdown of these costs is included in attachment 1.

1

Back-up data) and to include only the highlights or totals here. These highlights should sufficiently satisfy readers' curiosity so that they do not have to flip back to the attachment for more information.

(7) This paragraph is an implied **Objective.** In the previous paragraph Lorraine has listed three deficiencies inherent in the existing photocopier system, and now implies that her proposal will both correct these deficiencies and achieve a cost saving. (Although the diagram shows the Objective subcompartment to be at the start of the Proposal Details compartment, it is acceptable to move it forward and attach it to the end of the Background compartment, as Lorraine has done.)

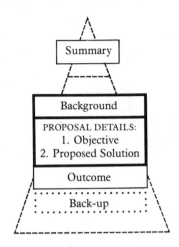

(8) Lorraine adds strength to her Objective by identifying a particular aspect needing correction. In effect she is saying, "We must have a copier that can take oversize originals and reduce them to fit onto a standard-size page." Later she will demonstrate that only the proposed system can do this.

(9) The **Proposal Details** compartment starts here with an analysis of alternatives. Normally the proposed solution (the author's "proposal") comes first and is discussed in detail. Alternative solutions follow, and are usually discussed in descending order of suitability. (Sometimes the sequence is reversed, but the reverse sequence is rarely as effective.)

Each alternative must be described factually and objectively. This is particularly important for the alternative the author proposes, because readers will automatically assume that the author favours it and is biased toward it. The analysis of each alternative should contain:

- a description of the alternative (copier system, in this case), including what it is, what it can do, and why it is being considered,
- an analysis of its strong features, or advantages (what is to be gained if the alternative is adopted), and
- an analysis of its weak features, or disadvantages (what it will cost, particularly if it will introduce negative side-effects).

(10) This paragraph contains the initial description of the proposed alternative, and refers the reader to two attachments where more com-

The four machines combined make about 34 000 copies a month, at speeds ranging from a slow 15 copies per minute to a moderately fast 40 copies per minute. They provide a reasonably good service at an average cost of 3.1 cents per copy. And yet none of the machines has the capability to:

* Print on both sides of the paper.

* Copy from oversize originals.

* Reduce the size of the copies.

(7) These features, which are available on newer, more expensive machines, would be useful additions to our copying services. In particular, they would enable us to achieve mailing economies by printing reports on both sides of the paper, and to reduce oversize computer sheets to fit on a standard page.

(8) Copying sheets of computer data has been a recurring problem. Either they must be retyped (a slow process, with the ever-present fear that errors may be introduced into the data), or copied in two passes, with the sheets subsequently taped together and folded into the report (also a slow process, with a cumbersome result).

(9) Proposed Photocopier System

(10) All the features we would like to have -- and more -- can be obtained by leasing an advanced-technology high-speed copier. The model I have investigated is the Vancourt Business Systems' PRO MK 3, which is a much-upgraded version of the PRO MK 1 currently used by the Marketing and Information Systems departments. It not only prints on both sides of the paper and copies from and reduces large size originals, but also produces 60 copies per minute and has an optional 20-station automatic collator. Its features and capabilities are compared to those of our existing machines in attachment 2, and a brochure describing the PRO MK 3 is in attachment 3.

The PRO MK 3 leases for $360 a month (without collator). If it were to replace the four existing copiers it would assume a monthly workload of slightly less than 34 000 copies, and I estimate its additional features would probably encourage us to make about 2000 more copies per month than we make now. The per-copy charge and materials costs for the 36 000 copies would amount to $504, for a total monthly cost of $864, or 2.4 cents per copy. This is $192 per month, or 0.7 cents per copy, less than we are currently paying.

A 20-station automatic collator can be attached to the PRO MK 3 for $70 per month, resulting in a total monthly cost of $934, or 2.6 cents per copy. This is $122 per month, or 0.5 cents per copy, less than we are paying now. The cost breakdown in attachment 1 compares the current and proposed costs in greater detail.

2

prehensive details may be found. Lorraine discusses costs in the two paragraphs that follow.

(11) The advantages are discussed only briefly here because Lorraine has already identified what features a new machine should have (at 7), has mentioned that the proposed machine has them (at 9 and 10), and has discussed the cost advantages (in the two preceding paragraphs).

Summary

Background

PROPOSAL DETAILS:
2. Proposed Solution
3. Other Solutions

Outcome

Back-up

(12) An analysis of the disadvantages starts here and continues for three paragraphs. It is much more detailed than the discussion of advantages because the author has to demonstrate that she has not only considered all the negative aspects, but also found methods for overcoming or negating them.

(13) Some authors prefer to write a short concluding statement at the end of each descriptive analysis, to sum up with a comment on the suitability of the particular alternative. Such a concluding statement is a reflection of the author's opinion, and hence has to be somewhat subjective. Other authors (and Lorraine is one of them) prefer to wait and present a combined descriptive analysis after they have described all the alternatives [see note (20)].

(14) Five other alternatives are considered, but only three have sufficient merit to warrant a detailed discussion. The two other alternatives are discussed briefly and then dismissed as being unnecessary or impractical, one at the beginning of this section (at 15), and one at the end (at 19).

(15) See note (14).

Having only one copier would mean consolidating all photocopying services in one location, which has both advantages and disadvantages. The advantages lie in more efficient copier management, better copier features, and lower operating costs. (Nearly all copier companies adjust their "per copy" charges according to the number of copies made each month: the more copies made, the lower the individual copy charge. For the PRO MK 3, the most significant price break occurs at 30 000 copies per month. Below 30 000, the charge is 1.7 cents per copy; above 30 000, it drops to 1.4 cents per copy.)

The disadvantages of a single-copier operation are the lost convenience of near-the-job copying and dependence on only one copier. Departments which currently have their own copier are likely to resist the proposed consolidation, although most will quickly recognize the advantages of the expanded features an advanced-technology machine would bring with it. Dependence on a single copier, however, needs to be examined more carefully.

Three factors have to be considered: machine reliability, the speed with which the manufacturer responds to service calls, and the ready availability of an alternative service in an emergency. Our experience with the PRO MK 1 has shown us good machine reliability and that the local office of Vancourt Business Systems consistently responds to service calls within four hours. As a further check I contacted Mansask Insurance Company and Remick Airlines, both of which use the PRO MK 3, and found their experience to be the same with the new machine.

Standby services can be provided in two ways. For routine copying we can retain the Aetna Little Gem, which the company owns, and use it for making average-quality copies. For important jobs we can take the work to Cathcart Copy Corner on the Mezzanine of this building, which we already use for long-run high-quality printing. Ms. Cathcart has guaranteed to give our work priority attention in an emergency, providing we give her 30 minutes notice. However, the need to use these standby services would be rare, since the speed of the PRO MK 3 would enable it to catch up quickly on backlogs following breakdown service or regular maintenance.

Other Systems and Configurations

In the early stages of my evaluation I studied photocopiers made by other manufacturers to identify whether they had better features or price advantages. I found that, on average, capabilities and prices were similar, and that there seemed to be no significant advantage in switching to a machine made by another manufacturer. The quality, reliability, and service performance we have experienced with the three machines we now lease (see attachment 2) convinced me that we should stay with products we know.

To achieve both a cost saving and better management of the existing copying services will mean reducing the quantity of copiers we now have and

3

(16) The three viable but less effective alternatives are described in what is probably a decreasing order of suitability, although the margin between them is small. Each is given a heading so that the alternative can be readily identified. In each case Lorraine describes the alternative very briefly, discusses its cost, and mentions its main strengths and weaknesses. She maintains an objective, impersonal tone throughout.

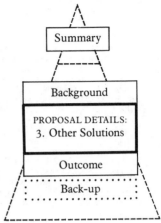

(17) Showing these tables of cost calculations is a useful way to demonstrate the similarity of cost for all three systems, and for readers to compare each to the total cost of the proposed system.

(18) The more remote or unlikely the alternative, the briefer the discussion and analysis may be.

consolidating those that remain into a "copying facility." The company-owned Little Gem should be withdrawn from service (other than being kept as a standby machine) because it is slow, costly, and produces copies on sensitized paper. And the remaining three copiers should be reduced to two, which would mean keeping only the two Fascopy machines, bringing in a second PRO MK 1, or retaining one of each. These alternatives are discussed below.

1. Two Valiant Fascopy Copiers

This is the most economical alternative, resulting in a total monthly cost of $834, which represents a per-copy cost of slightly over 2.4 cents.

Basic lease (2 @ $145)	$290
Charge per copy (34 000 @ 1.6¢)	544
	$834

The Fascopy provides high-quality copies on bond paper at a reasonably fast speed of 40 copies per minute. It does not, however, copy onto both sides of the paper, accept oversize images, or have a reduction capability. Neither can its copies be fed directly into an automatic collator. A summary of its features and capabilities is provided in attachment 2.

2. Two Vancourt PRO MK 1 Copiers

Two PRO MK 1 copiers would cost $918 per month, or 2.7 cents per copy.

Basic lease (2 @ $170)	$340
Charge per copy (34 000 @ 1.7¢)	578
	$918

The PRO MK 1 has an average speed of 30 copies per minute, copies onto only one side of bond paper, cannot accept large originals, and has no reduction capability. It can, however, be connected to a 10-station automatic collator, which can be leased for an additional $50 per month. With one collator, the monthly cost of two PRO MK 1s would increase to $968 or slightly more than 2.8 cents per copy.

3. One Fascopy and One PRO MK 1

Retaining one of each copier type permits an automatic collator to be included in the configuration, but offers no further advantages. The cost would be $876 without a collator, or $926 with a collator, resulting in a per-copy cost of 2.6 or 2.7 cents.

Basic lease (1 @ $145; 1 @ $170)	$315
Charge per copy (17 000 @ 1.6¢)	272
(17 000 @ 1.7¢)	289
	$876

4

(19) See note (14).

(20) So far, Lorraine's descriptions of the possible systems have been direct, factual, and objective. Now she has to compare the systems and demonstrate that the one she proposes is better than any of the alternatives. At this point her style changes from descriptive to persuasive. Although she may be personally convinced that the PRO MK 3 is the best system, she still has to convince her readers of this so that they will agree with her conclusions when they read them and accept her recommendations.

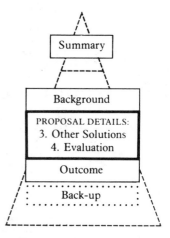

(21) By setting criteria at the beginning of the **Evaluation**, Lorraine provides a reference against which she can compare each alternative. If she had not first established the selection criteria she would have had to compare the alternative systems against each other, which would have been much more difficult to write briefly and convincingly.

The significance and validity of the selection criteria must be apparent to readers. It can be established here, or earlier in the proposal. (Lorraine established the reason for her criteria during her evaluation of the existing photocopying system.)

(22) A consolidated comparison table like this lets readers see a comparison quickly and easily. It would take many words to say as much.

(19) I also briefly considered the feasibility of retaining only one copier (most likely the Fascopy) and running it in parallel with an offset press. I discussed using an offset press with Ms. Cindy Cathcart of the Cathcart Copy Corner, who agreed that it would be useful for doing professional quality printing at high speed (up to 9000 copies per hour), but pointed out that to achieve high quality press work demands expensive ancillary equipment and hiring or training someone to run the press and the equipment. After a tour of her printing facility I discarded the concept of acquiring our own offset press as being both impractical and uneconomical for the comparatively small volume of printing we would need to do.

(20) ## Evaluation of Alternatives

To compare the alternative systems I identified four features or capabilities a new system preferably should have, and two features which would be advantageous but are less essential. The more important features are:

1. A significant cost saving.
2. The ability to copy from oversize originals and reduce them to fit on a standard size page.
(21) 3. High system reliability coupled with fast service.
4. High operating speed.

The two less essential features are:

5. Automatic feed to a collator.
6. The ability to print on both sides of the paper.

For a copier system without a collator, either the single PRO MK 3 or two Fascopy machines offer the lowest per-copy cost of 2.4 cents (see Table 1). With a collator, the lowest per-copy cost would be 2.6 cents, which is achieved only by the single PRO MK 3. These per-copy costs are considerably less than the current average per-copy cost of 3.1 cents.

TABLE 1: COST COMPARISONS FOR ALTERNATIVE SYSTEMS

(22)

System:	Existing	2 Fascopy	2 PRO MK 1		Fascopy + PRO MK 1		PRO MK 3[#]	
Monthly Cost:	$1056	$834	$918	$968[*]	$876	$926[*]	$864	$934[*]
Per-copy Cost:	3.1¢	2.4¢	2.7¢	2.8¢	2.6¢	2.7¢	2.4¢	2.6¢

* with collator
\# PRO MK 3 based on 36 000 copies per month; all others: 34 000 copies per month

5

(23) Lorraine makes sure that the expression "PRO MK 3" is noticed when each criterion is discussed. When more than one system meets the criterion, she always mentions PRO MK 3 first.

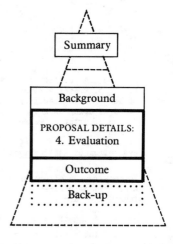

(24) The conclusions should evolve naturally from the proposal details which precede them. They should offer viable alternatives and must never introduce new information.

(25) A person writing a proposal cannot afford to write a weak recommendation. The recommendation must be strong and convincing, and clearly demonstrate that the author is personally sold on the course of action to be taken. The words "I recommend..." must be used rather than the impersonal "It is recommended that...," which seems to imply subconsciously that the author is not quite sure of himself or herself.

Only the PRO MK 3 has the capability to copy from oversize originals. It can accept originals up to 17 x 11 in. (43 x 28 cm), and can reduce any original by as much as 50%.

All three machines have satisfactory reliability records and good service reputations.

㉓ For the number of copies we make or are likely to make each month, a copier speed of 2400 copies per hour (40 copies per minute) would be acceptable. Both the PRO MK 3 and the Fascopy operate at this speed or better.

Only the Vancourt PRO machines accept automatic collators. The PRO MK 3 has an optional 20-station collator; the PRO MK 1 has an optional 10-station collator, which would be of limited use for the marketing manuals we assemble.

Only the Vancourt PRO MK 3 can copy onto both sides of the paper.

㉔
Conclusions

Consolidating our photocopier system can create considerable operating economies and provide an overall improvement in service. Of the four systems I evaluated, a single Vancourt PRO MK 3 can offer all the essential features and capabilities we desire. A two-copier Valiant Fascopy system would offer the same economies but would not be able to accept or reduce large-size originals such as computer printouts, or print on both sides of the paper.

㉕
Recommendations

I recommend that the company:

1. Lease a PRO MK 3 photocopier from Vancourt Business Systems Inc.

2. Terminate the leases on the three currently leased photocopiers.

3. Withdraw the company-owned Aetna Little Gem from service, and retain it as an emergency standby copier.

6

(26) There are three attachments to Lorraine's proposal:

- A cost comparison, on the facing page.
- A comparison of copier features and capabilities, on page 103.
- A brochure describing the proposed copier, which Lorraine obtained from the manufacturer's representative. (*Note*: attachment 3 has been omitted because it is too bulky to include here.)

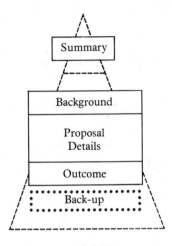

(27) How Lorraine tackled this proposal, and particularly the sequence in which she wrote it, are worth commenting on because they demonstrate the usefulness of writing a comprehensive proposal or report *in reverse order.*

1. A major part of the project was a physical evaluation of copiers, during which she became convinced not only that an alternative system was necessary but also which system was the best. Consequently she knew she would be writing her proposal with its outcome clearly in mind, and hence could not avoid being somewhat subjective. Yet she also knew that to her readers the detailed analysis of copier systems must appear objective (unbiased) even though it would lead to a foregone conclusion.

2. Lorraine's second step was to develop the two attachments seen here. Preparing them at this early stage had a significant advantage, in that it clarified her thinking. She had to identify the systems she would evaluate, the factors she would compare, and the categories she would place in each attachment (cost factors in one, and features and capabilities in the other). Doing all this drew the most important factors even more sharply into focus, and helped her organize the Proposal Details section.

3. At this point she drew up a rough topic outline, from which the headings in the proposal eventually took shape:

ATTACHMENT 1

COST COMPARISON: FOUR EXISTING COPIERS VS PROPOSED SINGLE COPIER

LOCATION	MODEL	MONTHLY RENTAL	COPIES PER MONTH	X	COST PER COPY*	=	COPY COST PER MONTH	TOTAL COST/MONTH	TOTAL COST/COPY
Existing Copiers									
Front Office	Valiant Fascopy	$145	13 500		1.6¢		$216	$ 361	2.67¢
Marketing & Information Systems	Vancourt PRO MK 1	$170	8 600		1.7¢		$146	$ 316	3.67¢
Production	Valiant Fascopy	$145	9 000		1.6¢		$144	$ 289	3.20¢
Purchasing & Supply	Aetna Little Gem	--	2 800		3.2¢		$ 90	$ 90	3.20¢
		$460	33 900				$596	$1056	3.10¢ (ave)
Proposed Copier:									
(Location to be selected)	Vancourt PRO MK 3 + Collator	$360 $ 70	36 000#		1.4¢		$504	$ 864 $ 70	2.40¢
		$430	36 000				$504	$ 934	2.60¢

* includes materials and cost-per-copy charge
\# estimated; based on better facilities creating increased usage

7

> SUMMARY: Propose a system which will be better and cheaper.
>
> BACKGROUND: What we have now; plus what we haven't got and really should have.
>
> PROPOSED SYSTEM: PRO MK 3 (how it meets all needs).
>
> ALTERNATIVES:
> - 2 Fascopy
> - 2 PRO MK 1   (the good
> - 1 of each   and bad
> - Offset printer   points of each)
>   plus copier
>
> EVALUATION: Establish criteria; compare systems to them.
>
> CONCLUSIONS: Best and second-best systems.
>
> RECOMMENDATIONS: Lease PRO MK 3; cancel existing leases.
>
> ATTACHMENTS: Costs, features, brochure of PRO MK 3.

4. She then started writing, beginning with the background and working steadily through the proposal details toward the conclusions and recommendations.

5. She had a draft typed, and then edited it.

6. Finally, Lorraine wrote the summary, selecting the key points from the draft proposal.

(28) An attachment, and particularly a comparative analysis, provides evidence which supports statements made in the proposal. This evidence must appear unbiased, otherwise the proposal will lose credibility. Facts and figures provide the necessary objectivity, but subjective comparisons such as "fair," "good," and "very good" sound like unsupported opinions unless their source is identified. For the three existing copiers the author is the source and her opinions are based on experience. For the unknown machine she has referred to two independent sources, both having experience with the machine.

(28)

ATTACHMENT 2

COMPARISON OF COPIER FEATURES

Features	Valiant FASCOPY	Vancourt PRO MK 1	Aetna LITTLE GEM	Vancourt PRO MK 3
Speed (copies/min)	40	30	15	60
Maximum size of original accepted	14 x 8½ in. (36 x 21.5 cm)	14 x 8½ in. (36 x 21.5 cm)	13 x 8 in. (33 x 20 cm)	17 x 11 in. (43 x 28 cm)
Copy quality	Very good	Very good	Good	Excellent*
Uses bond paper	Yes	Yes	No	Yes
Image reduction	No	No	No	Yes; down to 50%
Copies on both Sides of paper	No	No	No	Yes
Copies all colours	Yes	Yes	No; not light blue	Yes
Accepts a collator	No	Yes (10-station)	No	Yes (20-station)
Reliability record	Fair	Good	Very good	Good*
Fast maintenance service (4 hours)	Yes	Yes	No (2 days)	Yes*
Manufacturer	Valiant Office Products	Vancourt Business Systems Inc	Aetna Copiers Inc	Vancourt Business Systems Inc

* Opinions of two users: Mansask Insurance Company and Remick Airlines

8

The Formal Proposal

Formal proposals are normally lengthy documents which sometimes run to several volumes. Hence, their size prohibits a sample from being included here. Instead, a typical outline and the purpose of each compartment are described below.

Most formal proposals are written in response to a "Request for Proposal" (RFP) issued by the government or a large commercial organization. Normally time is short between the date an RFP is issued and the date the proposal must be presented to the originating agency. Companies submitting proposals each form a proposal team of key individuals, who work to ensure their proposal is written, illustrated, printed, and delivered before the closing date.

Many agencies issuing RFPs stipulate the major topics the proposing company must address, and the sequence in which information is to be presented. Unfortunately, although there is some similarity between the formats stipulated by different agencies, there are sufficient variances to

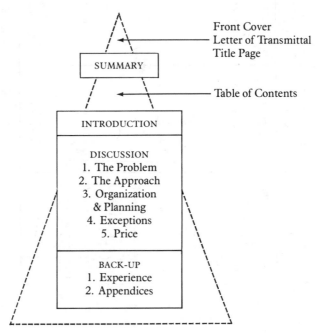

Fig. 7-3. *Typical writing compartments for a formal proposal.*

make it impossible to present a standard outline here. The outline illustrated below, therefore, is a simplified composite of several outlines, and is applicable to either a solicited or an unsolicited (i.e. company-initiated) proposal.

> Cover
> LETTER OF TRANSMITTAL
> Title Page
> SUMMARY
> Table of Contents
> INTRODUCTION
> DESCRIPTION OF WORK, PROBLEM, or SITUATION
> APPROACH TO WORK, PROBLEM, or SITUATION
> ORGANIZATION AND PLANNING
> EXCEPTIONS
> PRICE PROPOSAL
> EXPERIENCE:
>   COMPANY
>   EMPLOYEES
> APPENDICES

The major components of a proposal are illustrated in Figure 7-3. When the compartments are converted to headings they form an outline.

Letter of Transmittal

When attached to a formal proposal, a letter of transmittal assumes much greater importance than the standard cover letter pinned to the front of a semiformal or formal report. Normally signed by an executive of the proposing company, it comments on the most significant aspects of the proposal and sometimes the cost. As such it has a role similar to the executive summary which sometimes precedes a formal report (see chapter 8).

Summary

The summary mentions the purpose of the proposal, touches briefly on its highlights, and states the total cost. If a letter of transmittal is bound inside the report, the summary is sometimes omitted.

Introduction

As in a report, the introduction describes the background, purpose, and scope of the proposal. If the proposal is prepared in response to an RFP, reference is made to the RFP and the specific terms of reference or requirements imposed by the originating authority.

Description of Work, Problem, or Situation

This section describes the work that needs to be done, the problem that has to be resolved, or the situation that needs to be improved. It usually includes:

- a statement of the work/problem/situation, as defined by the RFP,
- an elaboration of the work/problem/situation and its implications (to demonstrate the proposer's full comprehension of the circumstances), and
- the proposer's understanding of any constraints or special requirements.

Approach to Doing Work, Resolving Problem, or Improving Situation

The proposer describes the company's approach to the work/problem/situation, states specifically what will be done and why it will be done, and then in broad terms outlines how it will be done. This section must be written in strong, definite, convincing terms which will give the reader confidence that the proposing company knows how to tackle the job.

Organization and Planning

Here, the "how" is expanded to show specifically what steps the proposer will take. Under "Organization" the proposer describes how a project group will be established, its composition, its relationship to other components of the company, and how it will interact with the client's organization. Under "Planning" the proposer outlines a complete project plan and, for each stage or aspect, describes exactly what steps will be taken and what will be achieved or accomplished.

Exceptions

Sometimes a company may conceive an unusual approach which offers significant advantages yet deviates from one or more of the client's specified requirements. These exceptions are listed and the reason why each requirement need not be met is clearly explained.

Price Proposal

The proposer's price for the project is stated as an overall figure and broken down into schedules for each phase of the project. The extent and method of pricing is often specified by the RFP.

This section of the proposal is the one most likely to be found in varying positions. The RFP may stipulate that it appear here, at the front, as the last section, or even as a separate document.

Experience

The proposing company describes its overall experience and history, and its particular experience in doing work, resolving problems, or handling situations similar to those described in the RFP. Key people who would be assigned to the project are named, and their experience is described in *curricula vitae.*

Appendices

The appendices contain supporting documents, specifications, large drawings and flow charts, schedules, equipment lists, etc, all of which are referenced in the proposal.

Proposal Appearance

Major proposals are multi-page documents assembled into book form and are usually bound by a multi-ring plastic binding. Minor proposals have fewer pages but are still bound or stapled into book form. Some very short proposals, particularly those submitted from one company to another, may be simply stapled together like a semiformal report, or even in some cases submitted as a letter.

Formal Reports

8

The Formal Report

Formal reports have a much more commanding presence than informal or even semiformal reports. Usually bound within a simple but dignified jacket, they immediately create the appearance of an important document. Internally, their information is compartmented and carefully spaced to convey confidence from start to finish.

The term "formal report" refers to the type of document rather than its title, and never appears on the title page. A formal report is more likely to be referred to as a feasibility study, an investigation or evaluation report, a product analysis, or a project report. Sometimes one of these names may precede the report's main title, but more often the name is omitted and the title stands alone (for example, the words "Evaluation Report" do not appear on the title page shown on page 119).

Traditional Arrangement of Report Parts

There are six main compartments in a formal report, the initial letters of which form the acronym SIDCRA (see Figure 8-1):

Summary
Introduction
Discussion
Conclusions
Recommendations
Appendix

The first four compartments are identical to the four basic compartments identified in chapter 2. If the writer of a formal report also proposes that

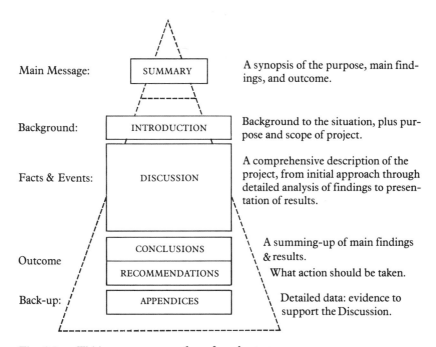

Main Message: SUMMARY   A synopsis of the purpose, main findings, and outcome.

Background: INTRODUCTION   Background to the situation, plus purpose and scope of project.

Facts & Events: DISCUSSION   A comprehensive description of the project, from initial approach through detailed analysis of findings to presentation of results.

Outcome   CONCLUSIONS   A summing-up of main findings & results.

RECOMMENDATIONS   What action should be taken.

Back-up: APPENDICES   Detailed data: evidence to support the Discussion.

Fig. 8-1. *Writing compartments for a formal report.*

action be taken, then the report has a Recommendations compartment. And if it contains supporting data, it has an Appendix.

The six main report parts identified in Figure 8-1 are the primary information-bearing compartments of a formal report. There are also additional parts which support these main compartments and they help give the report its formal shape. They are listed below in their appropriate positions in relation to the main compartments.

Cover Letter
Cover Page
Title Page
SUMMARY
Table of Contents Page
INTRODUCTION
DISCUSSION
CONCLUSIONS
RECOMMENDATIONS
References or Bibliography
APPENDIX
Back Cover

Guidelines for writing these parts appear on the following pages, facing the relevant sections of Guy Desrogers's report evaluating facsimile transmission for the owners of small businesses.

Alternative Arrangement of Report Parts

To meet the needs of executive readers, sometimes the Conclusions and Recommendations are brought forward so that they follow immediately after the Introduction. This rearrangement helps readers gain a more complete picture of the report's outcome without having to read all the details of the Discussion. Coincidentally, it fully completes the pyramid structure, as shown in Figure 8-2.

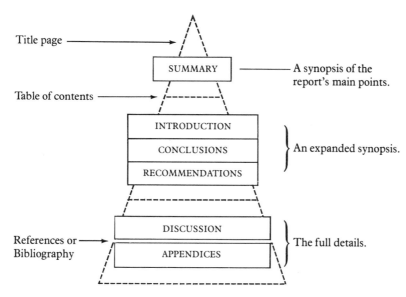

Fig. 8-2. *Alternative arrangement of writing compartments for a formal report.*

Moving the Conclusions and Recommendations forward does not materially affect the report's content, but does demand careful attention by report writers. They must ensure that:

• The transition from Introduction to Conclusions is achieved smoothly, naturally, and coherently.

• The Conclusions and Recommendations can be clearly understood (since their readers will not yet have read the Discussion).

• The Discussion does not start and end too abruptly. Since it is no longer preceded immediately by the Introduction or followed by the Conclusions, it will probably need a new introductory paragraph and an additional closing paragraph.

Analysis of a Formal Report

The following pages contain:

1. The letter from the client authorizing Assiniboine Business Consultants to carry out the study (Figure 8-3).
2. The cover letter accompanying the report (on page 117).
3. The report itself, with accompanying comments, from page 119 to page 144.

Cover Letter

A cover letter is really a transmittal document used to convey a report from one organization to another (or one person to another). The letter is paper-clipped to the *outside* of the report's front cover (in effect, the report is attached to the letter), and is not part of the report.

A cover letter can be a simple statement:

> I enclose our report No. 90/1 "Evaluation of Facsimile Transmission (FAX) for Use in Small Business Operations," which has been prepared in response to your letter of October 20, 1989.

Alternatively, it can offer a miniature summary, as Guy Desrogers's cover letter does.

ASBO (W)
WESTERN PROVINCES ASSOCIATION OF SMALL BUSINESS OWNERS
210 — 380 Broadway
Winnipeg, MB R3C 0T8

October 20, 1989

Ms Shelley M Kestner, President
Assiniboine Business Consultants Ltd
702 - 5 Donald St
Winnipeg MB
R3L 2T4

Dear Ms Kestner

At its meeting on October 9, 1989, the Administrative Committee of ASBO
(Western) authorized me to contract with your firm to study the advantages to
small business owners of purchasing facsimile machines (fax). They require
your report for distribution at the Association's annual general meeting in
Saskatoon on January 30, 1990.

The surfeit of literature on fax machines, coupled with numerous articles in
business journals and newspapers, has created both awareness and confusion
among the Association's members. Those who have taken the time to consult
with local salespeople have been given rather one-sided views of particular
product lines, while others in more remote locations are unable to obtain
information other than by mail. Both feel they want an objective analysis
that:

o   Describes what a fax machine can and cannot do.
o   Discusses the advantages and disadvantages of owning a fax machine.
o   Outlines the features a basic machine should have.
o   Outlines additional features available (options).
o   Analyses the features required for various size businesses.
o   Discusses costs generally, for various ranges of machines.

The members are not asking you to assess particular machines, since they feel
doing so would "date" the report too quickly. They want a general report that
they can refer to as a guideline before approaching potential suppliers.
(There are 5700 ASBO members, between Thunder Bay and Vancouver Island and in
the Yukon and Northwest Territories.)

I will need your report by January 16, 1990. Please supply eight copies for
immediate use, plus a set of camera-ready originals.

Sincerely

Deidre Parsons
Executive Director, ASBO(W)

Fig. 8-3. *Letter from a client requesting a study and report.*

Occasionally, an executive summary is used instead of the cover letter. An executive summary is considerably more detailed, in that it may discuss aspects which are of particular importance to management, such as financial considerations, or it may draw attention to unusual factors affecting the project and the ensuing report. An executive summary is always bound *inside* the report cover, so that it becomes an integral part of the report rather than a separate document.

Title Page

The title page contains four main elements:

- The full title of the report, which must be informative without being too long. Guy's title is informative; a very brief title such as FAX EVALUATION would not be useful.
- The name of the organization and sometimes the person for whom the report has been prepared.
- The name of the originating organization, and sometimes the name of the person who has written the report.

ASSINIBOINE BUSINESS CONSULTANTS LTD.
702 — 5 Donald Street
Winnipeg MB R3L 2T4

January 12, 1990

Ms Deidre Parsons
Executive Director
Western Provinces Association of
   Small Business Owners
210 - 380 Broadway
Winnipeg MB
R3C 0T8

Dear Ms Parsons

We have evaluated facsimile (fax) transmission of letters and
documents, as requested in your letter of October 20, 1989, and
have determined that many ASBO (W) members would find a fax
machine a useful addition to their office equipment.

Our attached Report No. 90/1, "Evaluation of Facsimile Transmission (Fax) for Use in Small Business Operations," shows that
facsimile transmission can be more efficient and less costly than
normal surface transmission of letters and documents, particularly in a local area. Our report also describes the range of
options available to purchasers of fax machines, and suggests
which options would prove most convenient to ASBO (W) members
without increasing the cost of a basic machine above $1500.

Eight copies of the report are enclosed, plus a set of camera-
ready reproducibles.

If you have questions regarding the report please call Mr Guy
Desrogers, our staff member who conducted the study, at 786 2245.

Regards

for Shelley M Kestner, President

enc
GR:rb

• The date the report is issued. If a report number is also included on the title page, it and the date are offset left and right as shown. If there is no report number, the date is moved to the centre.

A title page must have visual appeal, yet be simple and dignified. Every line must be centred individually on either side of a vertical centreline, which is offset about 8 mm (⅓ inch) to the right of centre page to allow for the unusable 12 to 20 mm (½ to ¾ inch) on the left-hand edge of each page (see Figure 8-4). This edge is usually covered by the binding or is punched for multiple-ring binders. If a report is printed on both sides of the paper, the binding edge on the reverse side of each sheet is on the right-hand edge of the page and the centreline is offset about 8 mm (⅓ inch) to the left.

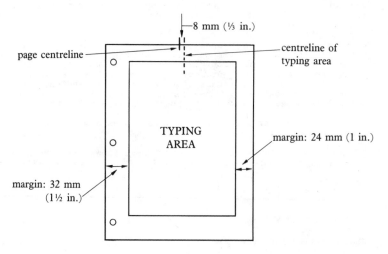

Fig. 8-4.   *The typing centreline is offset from the page centreline.*

ASSINIBOINE BUSINESS CONSULTANTS LTD.

EVALUATION OF FACSIMILE TRANSMISSION (FAX)
FOR USE IN SMALL BUSINESS OPERATIONS

Prepared for:

WESTERN PROVINCES ASSOCIATION OF SMALL BUSINESS OWNERS

Prepared by:

Guy Desrogers, B.A.
Business Consultant

Report No. 90/1   January 12, 1990

Summary

In a formal report the Summary follows immediately after the title page but before the Table of Contents. It always has a page to itself, and is centred on the page. Sometimes it is preceded by the heading ABSTRACT instead of SUMMARY.

The Summary is the most important page in the report. Because it is the first body of information that readers encounter, it has to encourage them to read further; if it does not, it has failed to achieve its purpose.

Guidelines for writing summaries are:

1. Write the Summary after the rest of the report has been written, but place it at the front of the report.
2. Draw information for the Summary from the Introduction (particularly the purpose of the project), the Discussion (pick out the most important highlights), and the Conclusions and Recommendations (the outcome or result of the project).
3. Keep the Summary as short as possible and make it interesting and informative. For example, rather than write "conclusions are drawn and a recommendation is made," state specifically what the main conclusions are and what you are recommending or suggesting should be done.
4. Keep the intended readers clearly in mind, to ensure you tell them what they most want to know or need to hear.
5. Use plain, non-technical words, and avoid topic jargon, so that the summary can be understood by almost any person who picks up the report.

You will probably revise the Summary more than any other part of a report.

SUMMARY

We have investigated whether it would be economically feasible for small business owners to invest in a facsimile transmission (fax) machine to send letters, documents and messages to customers and other businesses, rather than to continue using the conventional mail, courier, and telephone services.

Facsimile transmission offers ASBO (W) members a fast and inexpensive means for sending letters and documents, providing that (1) a sufficient number of their correspondents also have fax machines, and (2) the volume of documents they send is enough to warrant purchasing a fax machine. In many situations, sending a message by fax can be cheaper than conventional methods. If a small business owner is uncertain whether using fax is viable, we suggest leasing a fax machine for a trial period.

Table of Contents

A table of contents (T of C) is inserted at the front of a report mainly to help readers find specific information. But it also has a secondary, much more subtle purpose; that is, to let readers see how the author has organized the information and what topics are covered.

Readers who have read no more than Guy Desrogers's Summary can quickly establish his approach from the T of C. They will notice the logic of his organization, and how his three primary headings (between the Introduction and the Conclusions) show that he will:

• describe facsimile transmission,

• discuss its use from a small business owner's viewpoint, and

• analyze its suitability for the small business owner.

The subheadings show the specific aspects he will discuss. Knowing this arrangement in advance helps readers adapt more readily to the information presented in the Discussion which follows.

These are factors you should take into account when writing a T of C:

1. Every major topic heading in the report must also appear in the T of C.

2. The topic headings in the T of C must be worded exactly as they appear in the report.

3. Minor subordinate headings may be omitted from the T of C if their inclusion would make the T of C too lengthy or detract from the clarity of the overall organization plan.

4. The page heading often is more appropriately shortened to the single word CONTENTS.

5. All appendices must be listed, with the complete title drawn from the first page of each appendix.

6. If drawings or illustrations are grouped separately in the report, they should be listed in the T of C. If there are many illustrations, it is acceptable to insert the single entry "Illustrations" and page number in the T of C, and to place a separate list of illustrations as the first page of the Illustrations section.

CONTENTS

APPENDICES

Introduction

(1) The Introduction prepares readers for the details that follow in the discussion. It introduces them to the circumstances leading up to the project, and the reasons it was undertaken and the report was written. This is readily apparent in Guy Desrogers's Introduction, in which he briefly describes the history of electronic messages before he mentions the letter authorizing him to carry out a study of fax machines for small business owners.

An Introduction has three main components:

- **The Background**, which describes events leading up to the existing situation, what projects (if any) have been done previously, and why the project or study is necessary.

- **The Purpose**, which defines what the project or study is to achieve, who authorized it, and the specific terms of reference.

- **The Scope**, which outlines any limitations imposed on the project, either by the person(s) authorizing it or by the person undertaking it, such as cost, time in which the project is to be completed, depth of study, and factors which must be included or may be omitted.

Guy clearly follows the Background-Purpose-Scope sequence in his Introduction: paragraphs 1, 2, 3, and the first sentence of paragraph 4 form the Background, while the remaining five lines of paragraph 4 are the Purpose. Paragraph 5 (which is presented in point form) contains the Scope, which Guy has drawn from the client's letter of authorization (Figure 8-3).

Often, however, the sequence varies, sometimes with the Purpose appearing first and sometimes with the three components interwoven. In very long reports the three components may be treated as separate topics and preceded by individual subheadings.

<u>*EVALUATION OF FACSIMILE TRANSMISSION (FAX)*</u>
<u>*FOR USE IN SMALL BUSINESS OPERATIONS*</u>

INTRODUCTION

① As the computer age evolved in the late 1970s and through the 1980s, many businesspeople felt that the computer would take over as the primary conveyor of written mail. All that was needed, they reasoned, was for each person to have a computer on his or her desk, and for all the computers to be linked by a network. And so electronic mail, or "e-mail", was created.

But development was not as fast as the pundits had expected, for three reasons: many businesspeople felt uncomfortable about having to type at a computer terminal; there was incompatibility between the major computer systems, which inhibited the simple transmission of messages; and networks were not established as rapidly as had been expected.

Concurrently a second system was evolving, a system which permitted the transmission of a letter over telephone wires and for a copy to be printed out at the receiving end. This system was known as facsimile transmission, or "fax". However, initially fax did not create much interest because the cost of the early machines was high, errors tended to occur during transmission, and the quality of the printed image was marginal. But by the late 1980s the cost of fax machines had dropped, transmission loss had been reduced, and image quality had improved enough for some major businesses to adopt the system as a high-speed alternative to regular mail. Now, in 1990, businesses everywhere are purchasing fax machines.

Small business owners also have been aware of fax but have had difficulty in assessing whether a fax machine would be a useful purchase or only of marginal value. In a letter dated October 20, 1989, Ms Deidre Parsons, the Executive Director of the Western Provinces Association of Small Business Owners--ASBO (W)--commissioned Assiniboine Business Consultants Ltd. to evaluate the advantages of owning a fax machine and recommend whether one would be an economically viable purchase for the owner of a small business.

This report:

o   describes fax machines and how they work,
o   discusses the advantages of owning a fax,

1

Discussion

(2) The Discussion starts here. Note that:

- The word "discussion" seldom appears as part of a heading, and is never used as a single-word heading.
- The Discussion may follow immediately after the Introduction (i.e. on the same page, as has occurred here), or start on a fresh page. If it starts on a fresh page, it is customary also to start the Conclusions on a fresh page.

(3) To ease his readers gently into the Discussion, and at the same time allay their fears that he has written a report that is too technical, Guy starts immediately by comparing fax machines with office equipment his readers are familiar with.

(4) Illustrations such as drawings, sketches, and photographs provide a useful way to help readers visualize complex topics. (Guy realizes that the way facsimile transmission works is not really complex, but feels that a simple diagram inserted early in the report will also help allay readers' fears that his Discussion will be too technical for them to understand.)

Illustrations should be chosen and inserted with care, according to the following guidelines:

1. They should always serve a useful purpose.
2. They must supplement, not duplicate, the written words.
3. They must be simple, clear, and readily understood.
4. They must be referred to in the narrative of the report.
5. They should be accompanied by a brief caption or title, and sometimes a few explanatory remarks.
6. Ideally, they should be smaller than a full page, so that some text can appear either above or below them (full page illustrations tend to interrupt reading continuity).

More detailed information, particularly for preparing charts, graphs, and tables, is provided in chapter 12.

o   outlines the features a fax machine should have for use in a small
    business setting, and
o   discusses likely capital and operating costs.

It does not evaluate specific fax machines, because the market is changing
rapidly and new machines are being announced almost every month.

②   FACSIMILE TRANSMISSION OF DOCUMENTS

<u>How Facsimile Transmission Works</u>

③   Fax machines resemble office copiers. They have a slot for inserting the
    original to be transmitted (or a shelf for feeding in a series of originals),
    and a slot from which the copies are ejected as they are received and printed
    (and sometimes a shelf for storing them). Every fax machine can both send and
    receive facsimile messages.

If, for example, a person in Edmonton wants to send a purchase order to a
supplier in Montreal, he or she punches in the telephone number of the
destination fax. When the Montreal fax answers, the Edmonton fax automatically asks whether the Montreal machine is ready to receive a message.
If the Montreal fax responds affirmatively--also done automatically--the
Edmonton fax feeds the original purchase order under a photo-electric cell
that scans its surface a line at a time and converts what it "sees" into
digital signals. These signals are transmitted immediately over telephone
lines to the destination machine, where they are converted back into a
physical image and "burned" into heat-sensitive paper. The process takes
between 15 and 30 seconds, and is illustrated in Figure 1.

④

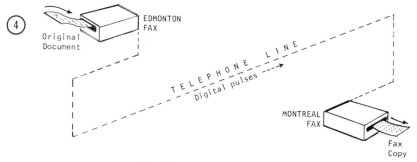

Fig. 1.   *Transmitting a fax message.*

(5) Having described how facsimile transmission works, Guy now turns to the fax machines themselves.

(6) Although Guy's language is simple, it does not talk down to readers. He uses terminology that any competent businessperson would understand.

(7) This is the first of six references Guy makes to information he has gleaned from other documents. He lists the documents in full at the end of the report (see report page 10 and comments (10) and (20)).

(8) How you arrange the information within the Discussion is extremely important. The overall logic of the case you present must be clear to readers, otherwise they may follow your line of reasoning with some doubt or hesitation. This, in turn, may affect their acceptance or rejection of your conclusions and recommendations.

Three factors can have a particularly negative effect on readers:

- Writing which is beyond their comprehension; that is, which uses technical terms and jargon they may not understand.
- Writing which fails to answer their questions or satisfy their curiosity; that is, does not anticipate their reactions to the facts, events and concepts you present.
- Writing which either underestimates or overestimates the readers' knowledge; that is, which assumes they know more (or less) about the topic than they really do.

These common pitfalls can be avoided if you clearly identify your readers. You have to establish first whether your report will be read primarily by management, by specialists knowledgeable in your field, or by "lay" people with very limited knowledge of your specialty. Then you must decide what they are most interested in, and what they need

(5) Types of Fax Machines

Fax machines can be divided into two groups: those that copy onto ordinary paper, and those that copy onto sensitized paper. The former produce a superior image similar to that made by a laser-jet copier, and are expensive. They are particularly suitable for businesses sending and receiving a high volume of fax messages, requiring copies that can be retrieved at any time in the future, or requiring high-quality copies that can be reprinted and used in company publications. Their cost starts at $5000.

(6) The latter produce a reasonable image on heat-sensitive paper that has a shelf life of only months or, at the most, two to three years. (If the paper is left in the light, its image fades over several weeks or months; in a dark storage place, such as a filing cabinet, the image lasts longer.) Consequently they are more suitable for businesses where the use of the message is transitory and the quality of image is not critical. They are also very much cheaper than fax machines using standard paper, with prices starting as low as $1200.

For most small businesses I am assuming that the less-costly fax machines producing images on heat-sensitive paper would be acceptable, if not preferred, and that if having a permanent copy of a particular fax message is important it could be made by copying the fax message on a regular office copier.

Advantages of Fax Transmission

The most significant advantage of facsimile transmission is that a business that owns a fax machine is much less likely to be affected by mail stoppages. A second advantage is that fax messages can <u>reduce</u> the cost of telephone calls. For example, a branch manager in Vancouver may take eight to ten minutes on the telephone to explain a hiring problem to head office in Toronto, whereas if the manager had summarized the details onto a short memorandum it could have been "faxed" in less than one minute, and both parties would have had a printed record to refer to. Similarly, a purchasing coordinator telephoning an urgent request for parts may need four minutes to give all the details (product descriptions, delivery address and method, purchase order number, customer number, and FOB instructions), and still would have to confirm the telephone request by typing and mailing a regular purchase order. If sent by fax, the purchase order would have been there in less than 30 seconds, and no follow-up would have been necessary.

(7) Sending a letter across town by fax is significantly cheaper than sending it by courier. "It can cost up to $16 to courier a couple of pages within the city," Ann Rhodes wrote in *Moneywise*[1], referring to Toronto, "but faxing costs the sender nothing if the call is not long distance; the recipient will pay about eight cents per page of paper used." And it is still cheaper to send a letter from coast to coast by fax rather than by Air Canada's *Airvelope* or

3

to hear from you (in case there is a conflict between what they would like to hear and what you need to say). And, finally, you have to plan your report so that the order in which you present information will answer not only their immediate questions but also any questions generated while they read.

For a start, go back to the terms of reference you were given by the person or organization authorizing your project. Pick out the points of most interest to your reader(s), jot them down, and then rearrange them into a logical sequence which will satisfy the readers' curiosity in descending order of importance.

(9) Although Guy's typist tried to arrange the typing so that it would start and finish at the same level on every page, on report pages 4, 5, and 9 this objective could not be achieved. At the foot of page 4, there are four blank lines. If the typist had brought the first line of type forward from page 5, he or she would have broken the first of three typesetting rules:

1. Never let a heading stand alone at the foot of a page.
2. Never allow the first line of a paragraph to stand alone at the foot of a page.
3. Never let the last line of a paragraph stand alone at the top of a page.

(10) Readers not only want to be given facts, but also want to know how they are derived. If it is not practicable for a report writer to provide an in-depth discussion of certain facts (possibly because they would be irrelevant to the report's main thrust or divert readers' attention), then reference must be made to the source from which the information was obtained. Such references are grouped and placed at the end of a report, where they are called "References," or simply "Endnotes."

The raised "4" in the middle of line 5 of paragraph two refers readers to the fourth item listed in the References on report page 10.

Canada Post's *Priority Post*, particularly if the fax machine can be programmed to send the message during the night when off-peak telephone rates apply.

The speed at which the message is transmitted is faster than any method other than e-mail. And even e-mail is slower if the originator is unaccustomed to typing at a computer terminal. If an immediate reply is needed, the receiver can write a response directly onto the document that has just been received and then re-transmit it to the original sender, a feature that is particularly useful when a draft of a document is sent for the receiver to edit or approve. This can provide extremely fast turn-around for a time-sensitive issue.

Portability is a third advantage of the smaller machines, which are no larger and no heavier than a portable computer such as the NEC *Multispeed*. The advantage of portability, however, is limited mainly to the transmission of documents, since other fax users could not send fax messages to the portable unit unless they knew where its owner planned to plug in the machine during his or her travels. Nevertheless, a portable fax would be useful for a traveller who needs to send a daily report to head office, or to order materials directly from a job site.

Disadvantages of Fax Machines

There are disadvantages, albeit minor ones. In all but the most expensive machines, photographs and drawings with fine or intricate lines do not transmit well. Although improvements are being introduced with each new model, it will probably be two or three years before the lower-priced machines have the technology to reproduce various fine shadings of grey. And the lower-priced machines also reproduce onto sensitized paper which, in addition to having limited image retention time, has a distinctive feel which some people dislike.

The transmission of confidential documents is also a problem, because most fax machines are kept in an open area where the documents they produce can be viewed by any person having reason to collect a document from the machine. Additionally, the courts have yet to decide the legality of signatures transmitted by fax, which could affect the legality of a signature on, say, a purchase order.

And, finally, repairs can be costly, as much as $800 if the scanning head fails. Most machines carry a one-year warranty, but after that the owner is advised to purchase a maintenance agreement which starts at $200 a year for the lowest-priced machine.

4

(*Note:* Footnotes, which once were popular, are not used in modern reports, partly because they distract a reader's eye but mostly because making room for them at the foot of a page creates typing problems. See chapter 11.)

(11) Extensive details, such as manufacturers' catalogues, tabulated data, calculations, specifications, and large drawings, are placed in an appendix and stored at the back of the report where they will not interfere with reading continuity. They constitute evidence which supports and amplifies what is said in the body of the report.

When selecting and referring to appendices, a report writer must ensure that:

- they are necessary and relevant,
- every appendix is referred to in the report narrative, and
- readers do not have to refer to the appendices in order to understand the report.

To prevent readers from having to flip pages and refer to appendices as they read, a report writer may have to include a synopsis of an appendix's highlights in the report narrative or draw a conclusion from the appended data. For example:

> A survey conducted in the Camrose shopping centre (see appendix K) showed that during weekdays 74% of shoppers travelled by private automobile, and 23% by bus. On Saturdays the number of automobile travellers increased to 83%, and bus travellers decreased to 15%. The remaining 2-3% travelled by bicycle or on foot.

(Appendix K contained seven pages of numerals; if placed in the report they would have both physically and psychologically interrupted the narrative.)

(12) This short paragraph is known as an "overview statement." It is inserted here to introduce a series of subparagraphs or short points. (Two more overview statements introduce the two further lists of fax features that follow.) To assume that a heading alone suffices to introduce a list is a mistake, since the abrupt transition unsettles readers. Readers feel much more comfortable and better oriented when a report writer leads them gently into the subtopics.

USING FAX IN A SMALL BUSINESS SETTING

When fax machines first started gaining popularity, it was thought they would be used primarily by large organizations. Yet a September 1989 survey of 427 businesses with less than eight employees reports that 42% of respondents consider their fax machine to be more useful than their telephone answering machine[2]. According to Kevin Kostash writing in *SBO Digest*, operators of single-owner businesses working out of their homes list the ability of some fax machines also to serve as a telephone answering machine as the most desirable feature[3].

⑩ Engineering consultants and architects, for example, find they are able to cut travel time and cost by conversing with clients, contractors, and suppliers by fax. They send out job specifications and drawings (using a high-resolution fax for the latter), ask for and receive quotations, and even bid on jobs themselves, all without leaving the office[4]. Even sales representatives, who would seem to have less use for fax because of their dependence on personal contact with customers, appear to be finding fax a fast means for placing orders with their home office (instead of mailing them in) and for following up with their customers to check that goods have been received[5].

The surveys mentioned earlier show that there is no clearly defined pattern of fax owners among small businesses, although businesses that communicate frequently by mail or by telephone with other organizations seem to benefit most from owning a fax machine. Of those in the service industry, businesses depending on procuring materials and spare parts are likely candidates, whereas those who provide a practical service such as painting and decorating probably have much less need for one.

⑪ Evaluation of the lower-priced fax machines currently available shows that they come with a wide range of features, some of which are essential for the small business owner while others are unlikely to be used. These features are described below and summarized in Appendix "A".

Essential Features of a Fax Machine

⑫ Few of the features in this category are options, since most are included as standard features on all but the very simplest fax machines. I consider all four to be essential for the small business owner.

> Compatibility. Fax machines have evolved through three levels or modes, known as Groups 1, 2, and 3 (Group 3 is the most recent). Machines purchased today must be compatible with Group 3, and ideally should be able to send messages to and receive them from the older Group 1 and 2 machines.

5

(13) Guy has a problem here. Normally he would place a list like this in an appendix so that it does not inhibit reading continuity. Then he would summarize the key points about the list in the narrative. But Guy feels that for this report his readers *must* have a clear but simple idea of what each feature does before they reach his analysis on page 8 of the report (under the heading "Weighing the Alternatives"). He also knows that it is a poor tactic to force readers to flip back to an appendix while they are reading the Discussion. So he compromises, maintaining a brief, coherent description of each feature in the report narrative, and placing a table consolidating all the features, together with their costs, in the Appendix.

(14) This is another overview statement, intended to orient readers before they start reading the details further on in the section. From it they will learn what the section is about and how the information is organized.

(15) Guy places cost details in an appendix and presents only the total costs in the analysis. To include a detailed cost analysis here would interrupt continuity because readers would be tempted to stop and study it. If they were to start comparing individual details at this point their attention could be easily deflected from the report's main thrust.

(16) Having presented the facts about facsimile transmission, and the various fax features available as options, Guy now discusses the alternatives open to the small business owner. This section will help his readers understand and accept the conclusions he will shortly draw, and the recommendations he will make. An analysis like this must always be part of the report's discussion, *never* part of the Conclusions.

Automatic Redial.   If the fax at the receiving end is "busy," the calling fax redials automatically at specified intervals until a connection is made, thus permitting the sender to concentrate on other work.

Originator Identification.   The sending fax automatically inserts the date, time, sending fax's telephone number, and the page number on each page printed by the receiving fax. This information usually appears as a "header" at the top of each page.

Confirmation Report.   The sending fax stores the originator identification details, and whether or not each transmission was completed successfully, for printing as an activity confirmation report.   These reports are maintained for both incoming and outgoing messages.

Useful but Less Essential Features

The six features described below offer added convenience but at greater cost. Some small business owners may consider them essential, while others may consider them to be only "nice to have."

Autodial. Often-used fax telephone numbers are stored in memory and are dialled automatically after the user depresses one or two buttons. Between 12 and 120 numbers can be stored, with the more sophisticated and higher-priced fax models holding the higher quantities.

Delayed Transmission.   The fax can be programmed to delay the transmission of messages until off-peak hours, when telephone rates are cheaper (often late at night).   The pages to be transmitted are stacked in a tray and are fed automatically into the machine.

Document Holder.   If several pages are to be transmitted, they may be stacked into a document holder that feeds them automatically into the machine (an essential feature if delayed transmission is being used), otherwise the user has to hand-feed the originals into the slot.   The number of pages that may be stacked varies according to the model's sophistication and price.

Shade Control.   Fax manufacturers are offering shade controls that can adjust the darkness to accommodate fine-line drawings and, to some extent, photographs.   The number of shades varies from 8 to 64, the cost increasing with the number of shades that can be selected.

Fault Reporting.   If an error occurs during transmission, such as incomplete pages being transmitted, an error report is immediately printed out so the sender knows the fault has occurred.

Non-Dedicated Line.   Some fax machines require a separate, or "dedicated", telephone line. Others have circuitry that permits them to share a line, thus reducing telephone line rental costs.

6

Marginally Useful Features

 The remaining eight features offer conveniences that probably would be unimportant to most fax users.

Paper Cutter. The individual sheets are cut automatically into page-size lengths as they are issued from the machine. Without a paper cutter, the pages appear as one long sheet which the user tears manually into page-size sheets.

Polling. On completing each transmission, the transmitting fax "polls" the receiving fax to ask whether it has perhaps already been programmed to send a fax later to the transmitting fax. If it has, the receiving fax automatically sends its message before terminating the telephone link.

Speaker. The dialling and telephone connection sounds are broadcast aurally, so that the user can hear whether or not the receiving fax has answered and is accepting transmissions.

Full Page Width. The fax prints to the full 8 1/2 inch width of the paper (most fax machines do not print the outer 3/8 inch at each side).

Size Reduction. Oversize originals (up to approximately 12 inches wide) can be accepted and are reduced photographically to fit onto the normal 8 1/2 inch wide paper.

Voice Announcement. The fax owner may record an announcement that tells regular telephone callers they have reached a fax line and asks them to dial an alternative number. This helps keep the fax line free for fax calls.

Confidentiality. A coding feature "scrambles" the transmission, which can be decoded only by someone authorized to read the message.

Plain Paper. The machine prints on plain paper rather than sensitized paper. The image is clear, black, and permanent, but the feature significantly increases the purchase cost.

Cost Considerations

The purchase price of a fax that prints on sensitized paper ranges from $1200 for a basic machine to about $4000 for a machine having about seventy percent of the options listed above. To include the "Confidentiality" feature would add a further $900 to the price. Appendix "A" includes a summary of approximate purchase prices for machines with various features. Leasing costs range from about $65 to $220 per month, with "Lease to Own" contracts being available from most manufacturers. If a machine is purchased, 15% of the purchase price can be written off as an expense in the year of purchase, and 30% in subsequent years.

7

The purchase price of a fax that prints on plain paper ranges from $5000 to $8000. Leasing costs range from $225 to $400 per month.

Operating costs for both types of machine are low. For example:

o   To transmit a fax, the only cost is the price of the long-distance telephone call. There is no cost to send a fax within the local telephone area.

o   To receive a fax on sensitized paper the cost is about nine cents a page, which represents the cost of each 8 1/2 x 11 inch sheet cut from the roll of paper. For a plain paper fax, the cost is about two cents a page.

A service contract which takes effect from the end of the warranty period costs about 10% of the purchase price per year, or about $150 a year for a fax costing $1500 to buy.

Business owners who prefer to establish the viability of facsimile transmission before purchasing a fax machine, can "test the water" first in two ways:

o   Initially, by using a nearby fax service provided by a local word processing house or printing company. The company providing the service charges a flat fee per page for sending and receiving messages, and then adds in the cost of long-distance telephone calls. Businesses using the service quote the service's fax number on their letterhead as if it were their own.

o   Subsequently, or alternatively, by leasing a fax on a rent-to-own arrangement, with the provision that all or a percentage of the lease payments can be applied to the purchase price if the business decides to buy the machine.

                        WEIGHING THE ALTERNATIVES

Most small businesses discover that, once they have installed a fax, they use it between 25% and 30% more than they predicted[6]. The difficulty, however, is to identify the right moment to purchase a fax, and the options to include.

The primary factor to consider is the amount the fax will be used. As a rule of thumb, if the business

o   frequently writes to or telephones other businesses,
o   often sends letters by courier, and
o   needs immediate responses to its communications,

8

(17) Report writers who have done a thorough project or study will have a clearly defined project outcome in mind. If they are to convince their readers that the outcome they describe is valid and the action they suggest is viable, eventually they must cease being purely factual and start persuading their readers to agree with their results. At this stage they can let their subjectivity show and their opinions become apparent.

Conclusions

(18) The Conclusions and Recommendations are sometimes referred to jointly as a "terminal summary," meaning that they provide a summing-up of the outcome of the discussion. It's unwise, however, to treat them both under a joint heading, because doing so can invite a report writer to inadvertently write a weak recommendation.

The most important thing to remember about Conclusions and Recommendations is that they must never offer surprises; that is, *they must present no new information*. Everything they contain must have been discussed in previous sections of the report (i.e. in the Discussion). Introducing a new idea or thought into the Conclusions or Recommendations is one of the common faults found in business reports.

The Conclusions and Recommendations can either follow directly after the end of the Discussion, as shown here, or start on a fresh page. If the Introduction has a page (or pages) to itself, then the Conclusions should also start on a new page.

The Conclusions should:

- be as brief as possible, with their main points drawn from the Discussion,
- be presented in descending order of importance; i.e. primary conclusion first, followed by subsidiary conclusions,
- satisfy the requirements established in the Introduction,
- never advocate action, and
- be presented in point form (in numbered subparagraphs) if there are many subsidiary conclusions.

Guy's conclusions may seem short, but they effectively answer the question posed by the client in her letter and repeated in paragraph 4 of the Introduction: "Is fax an economically viable purchase for the owner of a small business?"

then acquiring a fax is likely to prove advantageous. However, a prospective buyer should check first that the majority of the businesses's correspondents also have a fax.

Cost need not be a major concern, since the purchase price of a basic machine is comparatively low, all machines can be leased, and the cost of operation is negligible.

(17) Deciding which machine to purchase and the options it should have will depend on the type of business and the preferences of the purchaser.   The four features listed as "Essential" in a previous section certainly should be present. For a business sending faxes to mostly local addresses, the following features also would be useful:

> Autodialling
> A document holder
> A shade control with a minimum of 16 shades
> Fault reporting
> A paper cutter

(I have included the paper cutter, even though earlier in the report it is listed as one of the only marginally useful features, because for its low cost it offers a convenience I believe many business owners would consider worthwhile.)

The same five features would be equally useful for a business sending mostly long-distance fax messages, but the delayed transmission feature also should be included to reduce long-distance telephone charges.

CONCLUSIONS

(18) Facsimile transmission offers ASBO (W) members a rapid and economical means for sending letters and documents to customers and other businesses (providing the receivers of the communications also have a fax machine).

A basic fax machine complete with essential features can be purchased for $1200, or leased for as little as $65 a month. Machines with additional features cost from $300 to $1500 more but offer greater user convenience. Operating costs are negligible, particularly for local fax transmissions.

9

Recommendations

(19) The Recommendations should:
- be strong, and advocate action,
- use the active voice,
- satisfy the requirements established in the Introduction,
- follow naturally from the Conclusions,
- offer recommendations either in descending order of importance, or in chronological sequence if one recommendation naturally follows another, and
- be in point form if several recommendations are being made.

To make a strong recommendation, you should write "I recommend..." (if you are personally making the recommendation) or "We recommend..." (if you are making recommendations for a group of people, a department, or your company). Never use the weak, passive voice for a recommendation, as in "It is recommended that...."

Guy's Recommendations show *individual* small business owners the steps they need to take to identify whether fax is viable for their companies.

References/Bibliography

(20) A list of references or a bibliography catalogues all the documents the report writer used while conducting the project. Each reference describes the source of a particular piece of information, and in sufficient detail so that readers can identify and obtain the document if they want to refer to it.

There are two main differences between a list of references (which Guy uses) and a bibliography:
- References are numbered and appear in the sequence in which each piece of information is referred to in the report.
- Bibliography entries are not numbered and appear in alphabetical sequence of authors' names.

RECOMMENDATIONS

To determine the viability of purchasing a fax, we recommend that ASBO (W) members take the following steps:

1. Identify the quantity of messages they are likely to send by facsimile transmission, then add 25% to the figure.

2. Determine whether sufficient potential recipients of their fax messages already have or plan to acquire a fax.

3. Calculate the difference in cost for sending the planned messages and documents by fax instead of by mail, courier, or telephone.

4. Determine whether sending messages and documents by fax offers a real advantage to their business operations.

If their assessment shows that facsimile transmission is viable, we also recommend that ASBO (W) members:

5. Consider the available fax options and identify which would be essential for their business.

6. Assess whether they should purchase a fax machine outright or lease one initially on a rent-to-own basis.

REFERENCES

1. Ann Rhodes, "Is That a Fax?", Financial Post Moneywise, February 1989, p 66.

2. Valerie K Halston, Survey of FAX Users in Canada, April-June 1989. Report 89/07, Multiple Industries Ltd, Calgary, Alberta, September 29, 1989, p 13.

3. Kevin M L Kostash, "Chatting it Up with Fax", SBO Digest, 12:11, November 1989, p 62.

4. Kostash, p 66.

5. Halston, p 9.

6. Marylin T Koryluk and David Weston, Electronic Messaging in Canada (Toronto, Ontario: Astro-Weston Books Limited, 1988), p 173.

10

Generally a list of references is more common in business and technical reports, and bibliographies are seen more often in professional journals and academic theses.

Some suggestions for writing a list of references or a bibliography are contained in chapter 11.

Appendix

(21) The Appendix contains complex analyses, statistics, manufacturers' data, large drawings and illustrations, photographs, detailed test results, cost comparisons, and specifications—indeed, any information which if included in the discussion would interrupt reading continuity. Often an appendix will contain detailed evidence to support what is said more briefly in the discussion. And sometimes the appendix section contains more pages than all the remaining sections of the report put together.

Certain guidelines apply to appendices (or "appendixes"—either plural is correct):

- Appendices always appear in the order in which they are first referred to in the report (and, of course, every appendix must be referred to).
- As appendices are considered individual documents, each may be paginated separately, starting at "1".
- Each appendix is assigned an identifying letter; that is, "Appendix A," "Appendix B," etc.

Note: To save space in this book all but the first page of Appendix "B" have been omitted because they contain only numerous, detailed lists.

Because each appendix is a separate document, sometimes an appendix may contain its own references. The references may be listed at the end of the appendix or treated as a footnote.

㉑

APPENDIX A

STANDARD AND OPTIONAL FAX FEATURES

The features listed below are those most often offered by manufacturers of fax machines. They are divided into three groups: those normally found on all machines; those, although not essential, that would be useful to have; and those that are only marginally useful.

The three boxes in the right-hand column represent the *approximate* cost of the features identified as desirable for a small business (i.e. marked "X"). For example, the approximate total cost for a fax to be used for mainly local transmissions would be:

$1200 + $400 + $80 = $1680.

For mainly long-distance transmissions the cost would be about $100 more.

Feature	Recommended Options Local ** Dist.		Approx Cost
Essential (Normally Standard) Features			
o Compatibility	X	X	
o Automatic Redial	X	X	$1200
o Originator Identification	X	X	
o Confirmation Report	X	X	
Useful Features			
o Autodial	X	X	Local:
o Delayed Transmission		X	$ 400
o Document Holder	X	X	
o Shade Control	X	X	Dist.:
o Fault Reporting	X	X	$ 500
o Non-dedicated Line			
Marginally Useful Features			
o Paper Cutter	X	X	$ 80
o Polling			
o Speaker			
o Full Page Width			
o Size Reduction			
o Voice Announcement			
o Confidentiality			
o Plain Paper			

** Local = Features desirable for mainly local fax transmissions
   Dist. = Features desirable for mainly long distance transmissions

APPENDIX B

CURRENT MODELS AVAILABLE FROM FAX MANUFACTURERS

These pages list the manufacturers of FAX machines sold in Canada, and the range of models each manufacturer offers (as of January 1, 1990). Small business owners should use this list only as a general guide, since new models are being released almost monthly.

NOTE

The 13 pages that make up this appendix have been omitted to save space.

Guy Desrogers's Report Writing Sequence

The sequence in which Guy wrote his report is worth examining:

1. He prepared Appendix A first. (He did not label it then as Appendix A, for he did not yet know where it would fit within the report.) Formulating this list forced him to decide which factors he considered would be most useful to small business owners.

2. He dealt next with the facts, writing almost all of the Discussion, but not in the order in which the parts appear in the finished report. First he wrote the section titled "Using Fax in a Small Business Setting," which included the descriptions of optional fax features and the cost considerations. Then he wrote the general description of facsimile transmission, drew the sketch, and outlined the advantages and disadvantages of using fax.

3. Now he had to turn to the more subjective task of identifying what he felt a small business owner would need. First he wrote the Introduction, so that he could establish his criteria. Next he wrote the "Weighing the Alternatives" section of the Discussion, ensuring that either here or in earlier parts of the Discussion he covered every aspect he would subsequently sum up in the Conclusions and Recommendations. Then he wrote the Conclusions, which he was surprised to find could be stated very briefly since they were well supported by the preceding sections. He followed these with his Recommendations, placing himself mentally in a small business owner's shoes and answering the question: "What should I *do* to find out if I should invest in a fax?"

4. Finally, he wrote the Summary.

PART FIVE

Report Writing Techniques and Methods

9

Appearance and Format of Letter and Memorandum Reports

The appearance of the reports you write should demonstrate the quality of your words. A neatly presented report, in the format proper to the circumstances and the intended reader, will create the impression that you are presenting valuable information. In the reader's eyes it will enhance your credibility as a reporter of information, even before he or she starts reading.

Conversely, a shoddy-looking report will create the impression that you are a careless writer whose information is of doubtful accuracy. And readers will gain this impression as soon as they pick up your report, before they have read a word!

This chapter will help you choose the proper shape for each report you write, and present it in a way that will subtly encourage readers to accept your facts and figures. There are four formats to choose from:

- A **memorandum**, which is used when a report is directed from one person to another within the same organization. The memorandum is the most informal form of report presentation.

- A **letter**, which normally is used when the writer of the report belongs to one organization and the person to whom it is directed belongs to another. Letters are more formal than memorandums, but are still an informal reporting medium.

- A **titled document**, in which the report's title and the author's name are centred at the head of the first page, with the report narrative starting beneath them. Because its appearance is slightly more formal than that of a letter report, a titled document is often referred to as a *semiformal report*.

- A **bound document**, with a cover and full title page preceding the report proper, and separate pages for individual sections such as the Summary and Table of Contents. Such reports are known as *formal reports*.

148

Guidelines for presenting informal and semiformal reports in the correct format are outlined in the sample memorandum, letters, and the first page of a semiformal report illustrated in Figures 9-1 through 9-4 of this chapter. Guidelines for presenting a formal report are included with the report analysis in chapter 8.

H. L. Winman and Associates Ltd.

INTER - OFFICE MEMORANDUM

From: R Bryant Date: June 26, 19xx

To: W K Carter **Subject:** Format for memorandum reports

cc L L Sampson

Informality should be the keyword for your memorandum reports, both in appearance and language. The appearance should be simple, with the salutation and signature block omitted.

Informality, however, should not be interpreted as a signal that you can use sloppy language. Your reports must be organized coherently; your paragraphs and sentences must be properly constructed; and the words you use must be simple and clear.

You may use subparagraphs (point form) to break up long paragraphs or to list a series of points, as shown below. And if a report is long you may insert headings to help readers see how you have organized your information. Other factors you should be aware of are:

1. The subject line should be <u>informative</u>, so that it gives a clear indication of the memorandum's contents. "Memorandum reports" would not have been sufficiently informative as a subject line for this memorandum.

2. The first line of each paragraph may be indented five spaces or started flush with the left-hand margin.

3. The names of persons who are to receive carbon copies of the memorandum may appear directly under the addressee's name (as has been done at the top of this memorandum) or entered three lines below the last paragraph, against the left-hand margin.

You may either sign or initial a memorandum report.

Rod Bryant

Fig. 9-1. *The shape of an informal memorandum report.*

VANCOURT BUSINESS SYSTEMS INC

27 September 19xx

(A) Mavis J. Morgan
Manager, Customer Services
Cameron Manufacturing Limited
(B) 2820 Border Road
London, ON
N6B 3K5

(C) Dear Ms. Morgan:

(D)   Letter Reports in Modified Block Format

The modified block format is the more conservative of the two letter styles currently used by business and industry. Because it does not appear to be as severely businesslike as the full block format, it is particularly suitable for writing to the public.

Both the left-hand margin and the page centreline are used to position the various parts of the letter horizontally. For example:

1. The name and address of the person you are writing to are typed flush with the left-hand margin ("flush" means all lines start at the margin).

2. The first line of each paragraph may start at the margin or be indented five characters (letter spaces), as has been done here.

3. The date and the signature block start at the page centreline.

4. The subject line is centred on the page centreline, and normally is underlined.

5. The left- and right-hand margins are roughly the same width.

If the report is short enough to fit on one page, it should be positioned vertically so that the body of the letter is roughly in the middle of the page.

(C)   Sincerely,

Martin Cartwright

Martin Cartwright
Publications Editor

MC:rn

Fig. 9-2.   *The shape of a letter report in modified block format.*

18 March 19xx

File: 276-13

THE RONING GROUP

Communication Consultants
Box 181, Postal Station C
Winnipeg Manitoba
Canada R3M 3S7
(204) 452-6480

(A) Mr R Craig Williams, Head
Corporate Resources Division
Centaur Corporation
(B) PO Box 2760
Vancouver BC
V6C 2P9

(C) Dear Craig

(D) The "Full Block" Letter Format

My analysis of 300 major companies in Canada and the U.S. shows that
246, or 82%, prefer the full block letter style for their corporate
correspondence and informal letter reports.

In the full block format every line starts at the left-hand margin,
which simplifies typing because no lines have to be measured and
positioned about the page centreline. However, shorter (one page)
letter reports have to be carefully centred vertically on the page if
they are to achieve a balanced appearance.

Because it conveys the impression of a modern, forward-thinking organization, I recommend you adopt the full block style for the Centaur
Corporation's correspondence.

(C) Regards

Marilyn P. Duvall

Marilyn P Duvall, Specialist
Business Communications

MPD:es

Fig. 9-3. *The shape of a letter report in full block format.*

(A) It is customary to name the person to whom a letter is addressed first, and to follow the person's name with his or her title and then the name of the company or organization. The position the person holds may be placed in the second line (as in Fig. 9-2) or beside the person's name (Fig. 9-3).

(B) Punctuation is omitted from the recipient's address, except where a comma is needed to separate two unrelated words in the same line. Although it is more common to insert a period after "Mr.", "Ms.", and a person's initials, there is a trend to omit such punctuation.

(C) The use of a colon (:) after the salutation and a comma (,) after the complimentary close is optional, but their insertion or deletion should be consistent.

(D) Subject lines are optional. If used they should be underlined, and may be preceded by "Subject:", "Ref:" or "Re:" (also optional).

①

PREFERRED FORMAT FOR SEMIFORMAL REPORTS

②

Rodney T. Elson
Communications Consultant

Summary

③

The appearance of a semiformal report lies half way between the comfortable informality of the letter report and the strict formality of the
formal report. The report's title is given prominence by being displayed
in capital letters across the upper centre of the first page, and the
author's name and company affiliation are centred neatly beneath it. The
narrative of the report follows immediately, and continues onto subsequent pages. The impression gained by the reader on first seeing the
report should be of a quality document containing important information.

④

The Report's Parts

The parts of a semiformal report are similar to those of a formal report,
except that the report normally has no cover, the summary seldom has a
page to itself, and the table of contents page is omitted. As in a formal
report, each major section is introduced by a centre or side heading.

Fig. 9-4. *The appearance of a semiformal report (top of first page only).*

(1) The report title should be positioned about 40 to 50 mm below the normal top line
of typing (i.e. about 75 to 90 mm below the top edge of the page), to make the first
page appear better balanced and less forbidding.

(2) The author's name and affiliation may appear either here or on the last page of the
narrative (i.e. ahead of the attachments).

(3) The first line of each paragraph may be indented five spaces or may start at the left-
hand margin, as in Figure 9-4. The latter method is preferred.

(4) To create an uncrowded appearance there should be 1½ or 2 blank lines between
paragraphs, but only one blank line between a heading and the paragraph that follows
it. See Lorraine Dychuk's proposal on pages 89 to 103 for an example.

To speed up long-distance communication, many organizations now send their reports by facsimile (commonly known as FAX). A report sent by FAX is transmitted over telephone lines and is received virtually immediately. The transmitting FAX machine converts the paper image into digital signals which, when heard by the receiving FAX, are converted back into the original image and printed on paper.

When sending a report by FAX you should precede it by a single sheet that lists the name and telephone number of both sender and receiver, and—most important—lists the number of pages being transmitted so that the person at the receiving end can check that he or she has received the entire document. An example of a FAX transmittal page is shown in Figure 9-5.

RGI VIDEO PRODUCTIONS

569 Oxford St.
Winnipeg MB Canada R3M 3J2
(204) 488 7060

FAX MESSAGE

TO: Multiple Industries, Toronto

FAX NO.:   416 493 0078

ATTENTION: Don Gershtein, Ext 302

DATE: February 04, 19xx   *TIME:*   14:35

NO. OF PAGES (including this sheet):   7

BRIEF MESSAGE:

Don:

I am attaching a recent report which shows
that FAX is more user-friendly than E-mail for
companies such as ours, where communicating
between remote offices thousands of miles
apart is important.

Particularly note the warning on page 4, which
points out that every FAX message should be
preceded by a cover page like this on which
addressing details and the number of sheets
are listed.

This square and the italicized words are
stored in a computer file ready for the user
to type into, as I have done here.

Ashley Cairns

REPLY TO: RGI FAX No.:   204 475 3092

If not all pages received, call:
FAX No.   or 204 488 7060

Fig. 9-5.   *A transmittal page for a document to be sent by facsimile (FAX).*

(A) The addressing instructions list the name and FAX telephone number of the receiving organization, and the name of the person the FAX is to be routed to.

(B) Writing something in the "Brief Message" block is optional. All other entries *must* be filled in.

(C) An alternative telephone number is provided, in case the FAX line is inoperative or overloaded.

10

The Language of Report Writing

We use essentially the same language for report writing as we do for regular correspondence, and in both cases we strive to be brief yet fully informative. A report must contain all the information its readers need to understand a given situation and if necessary take action, and yet it must neither waste the readers' time by conveying too many details nor obscure the message by using ponderous sentences and paragraphs. This chapter describes techniques which will help you focus your reports correctly, be direct, and avoid cluttering the narrative with unnecessary words and expressions.

Get the Focus Right

The first rule of report writing is never to start writing until you have answered these three questions:
1. Who is my reader?
2. What is the purpose of my report?
3. Do I want to be purely informative or convincingly persuasive?

Your answers will give you a sense of direction, and help you write much more easily and spontaneously than if you had simply picked up a pen and started writing. The implications of each question are outlined below.

Identify the Reader

Kim Wong has been studying materials-handling methods used by her company and reckons there is a better way to manage the ordering, receiving, documenting, storing and issuing of parts and materials. Her department manager, Anna Sharif, has told Kim that she is to write a report of her findings and recommendations, but has omitted to tell her who will be reading the report and using the information it contains.

Kim is likely to make many false starts if she tries to write without a clearly defined audience in mind. Without a known target, she will write in a vacuum and will be unable to focus her report. She cannot *assume* she is writing only for Anna's eyes, since Anna may be planning to send the report directly to head office with an accompanying memorandum. Kim's report would then be read by a much wider audience. To focus her report properly Kim needs to find out not only who is going to read it but also how it will be used.

Identify the Purpose

Always check that you have clearly identified the purpose of your report before you start writing. Try writing the words

"The purpose of my report is..."

on a separate sheet and then completing the sentence (but limit yourself to only one sentence). Kim Wong, for example, should write

> The purpose of my report is to demonstrate that our materials-handling methods are outdated, and to show how they can be improved.

Kim's next step is to decide whether her report is to be informative or persuasive (i.e. if it is to "tell" or to "sell"). When a report writer is simply informing readers of a given situation, then the sole purpose of the report is to present facts; but if the writer wants to evoke a response to a situation, then the report must convince readers that the writer has a valid point, and persuade them to act. If Kim knows that the department manager will be her only reader, and that Anna is only seeking facts, then she will write an informative report telling her what she has found out. Alternatively, if she has discovered that her report will be sent to head office to persuade executives to invest in a new materials-handling system, she will have to write a persuasive report because she has to "sell" the new system to head office.

Write to Inform

Informative writing is much simpler than persuasive writing. To write informatively you need to present facts clearly and in logical sequence. You should write briefly, directly and forthrightly, closely following the pyramid structure described in chapters 2, 3, and 4. The pricing error report on page 21, and the mobile trailer progress report on page 47, are typical examples of informative writing.

Write to Persuade

The difficulty with persuasive writing is preserving one's objectivity. Although your aim should be to convince readers to accept your ideas, your partiality or bias should not be so obvious that readers feel they are being coerced.

Fortunately, several sections of every persuasive report deal with facts, and these can still be presented informatively. These are the Introduction, in which you describe the background to your report, and the description of your Approach and Findings. (Kim Wong's description of the existing materials-handling methods, for example, should be strictly informative regardless of whether she is writing a "tell" or "sell" report.) Only when you have to present your suggestions and analyze advantages and disadvantages should your involvement become obvious. Of course, when you make a recommendation your preference should be readily apparent.

The suggestion and proposal in chapter 7, and the formal report in chapter 8, are examples of persuasive writing. The two longer reports, particularly, show how their authors have gradually developed their cases, working carefully from an informative presentation of facts toward a persuasive evaluation of alternatives.

Be Direct

Chapters 2 through 8 stress the need to satisfy a reader's curiosity by identifying the most important information, consolidating it into a short summary statement, and placing it at the front of every report you write. This "direct" writing technique can be extended to individual sections of a report and to each paragraph. It can also be enhanced by writing as much as possible in the first person and in the active voice.

Use the Pyramid Structure

There is no need to feel that the pyramid structure described in chapter 2 applies only to a complete document. Within a long report each major section should also be structured "pyramid style," with each section opening with a short summary statement followed by the basic BACKGROUND-

FACTS-OUTCOME arrangement of information. This technique is even used in this chapter: the opening paragraph of each major subsection starts with a summary statement. For example, the heading GET THE FOCUS RIGHT on page 156 is followed immediately by this short paragraph:

> The first rule of report writing is never to start writing until you have answered these three questions:
> 1. Who is my reader?
> 2. What is the purpose of my report?
> 3. Do I want to be purely informative or convincingly persuasive?

These five lines identify the topics discussed in the remainder of the subsection.

Similarly, the first paragraph of *this* subsection (immediately following the heading BE DIRECT) summarizes what is being described here and on the next few pages.

The pyramid can even be used to structure paragraphs. The first sentence becomes the topic sentence (Summary Statement), and the remaining sentences amplify and develop the initial statement. For example, in the two paragraphs that follow, the topic sentences (in italics) describe the main point while the remaining sentences provide more details.

1. *We have evaluated the condition of the Merrywell Building and find it to be structurally sound.* The underpinning done in 1948 by the previous owner was completely successful and there still are no cracks or signs of further settling. Some additional shoring will be required at the head of the elevator shaft immediately above the 9th floor, but this will be routine work that the elevator manufacturer would expect to do in an old building.[1]

2. *The costs of poor communication are seldom calculated but should never be overlooked or simply brushed aside.* An inadequately worded purchase order which results in the wrong goods being delivered can increase the cost of doing business and involve countless people in correcting the error. Inadequate directions for an appointment, which cause one or more persons to go to the wrong rendezvous and to waste time, are equally costly. So are erroneous facts or ambiguous calculations which create disagreement—if not outright conflict—between the transmitter and receiver of the information.[2]

In high school and college or university you were probably told that every paragraph must have a topic sentence, and that it can either be implied, or placed as the first sentence, the last sentence, or as both the first and last sentence of the paragraph. For report writing—and particularly for short reports—you would be wise to place your topic sentence at the beginning of each paragraph. This approach helps your readers to discover quickly what each paragraph is about, and so grasp more readily the details that follow.

As your experience as a report writer grows, you will undoubtedly learn to use non-pyramid paragraphs in longer reports. But remember that for short, informative reports the pyramid style paragraph (i.e. with a topic sentence at the beginning) is more direct and more effective than the non-pyramid paragraph. Non-pyramid paragraphs are more suitable for long persuasive reports, but even then they need to be used only occasionally, to create a particular effect. For example, the events described in the following paragraph lead up to the main point the author wants to make (in the italicized topic sentence).

> We first monitored sound levels between 8 p.m. and 10 p.m., to establish a background sound level while the building was empty. Then the following day we measured sound levels hourly from 7 a.m. to 6 p.m. at 28 locations throughout the building, and recorded the results in appendix B. Seventeen of the measuring points were in or adjacent to departments where employees had complained of excessively high noise, and eleven were control points in departments from which no complaints had been received. *Although the sound levels measured at the "noisy" locations were on average 7 decibels higher than at the control locations, at no location was the sound level higher than 63 decibels.*

This climactic method (leading up to the main point) can be useful if you have to prove your case to readers who may be prejudiced against or tend to resist the facts you have to present. But the same information can be presented just as easily in the pyramid style to readers who are better prepared to accept the facts.

> *We monitored sound levels and found that they did not exceed 63 decibels anywhere in the building, although the sound level for departments reporting excessively high noise was an average 7 decibels higher than the sound level for other departments.* Our measurements were recorded on two separate occasions: between 8 p.m. and 10 p.m. one evening to establish a background sound level while

the building was empty, and hourly from 7 a.m. to 6 p.m. the following day. Seventeen of the 28 measuring points were in or adjacent to departments where employees had registered complaints, and eleven were control points in departments from which no complaints had been received. The results are shown in appendix B.

Which approach you use will depend on the effect you want to create.

Write in the First Person

Reports are written and read by people, so it is natural to write from person to person. Yet many report writers try to avoid using the first person when they write because they feel they are being "unbusinesslike" or "unprofessional." They write

> The components have been ordered...
> A data survey was conducted...
> A report was submitted...
> It is recommended that...

The writers of these statements seem afraid to say they were involved in ordering the components, the data survey, the report submission, and the recommendation. Their statements would be much more direct and effective if a "person" could be inserted into them.

> **I** have ordered the components...
> **We** have conducted a data survey...
> **I** submitted my report...
> **I** recommend that...

To write in the first person (i.e. to use "I," "we," "me," and "my") is not unprofessional or unbusinesslike. When you write a report to your manager, to someone in another department, or to someone outside your own organization, you should try to write from person to person. Insert "I" if you are writing for yourself, and "we" if you are reporting for a group of people, your department, or your company.

If you are drafting a report for another person's signature (your department head, for example), you may feel you do not have the right to use "I" and "we." Under these circumstances you should go to the person whose name will appear on the report and ask if you can use the first person.

There are numerous examples of reports written in the first person throughout chapters 3 through 8. The pronoun "I" is readily evident in the informal memo reports in chapters 3 and 4 (particularly see Frank Crane's trip report on page 25, Marjorie Franckel's progress report on page 42, and Tom Westholm's investigation report on page 52). Only in the slightly more formal inspection report on page 33 and progress report on pages 47 and 49 is "I" less evident: Paul Thorvaldson has limited its use primarily to his suggestions (his Outcome compartment), and Roger Korolick uses "I" only when he refers to his concerns and plans.

In the longer reports, the first person singular ("I") is used by Lorraine Dychuk in her in-house proposal on pages 89 through 103, but Tod Phillips prefers to use the plural "we" throughout his client-oriented investigation report (pages 71 through 79). Guy Desrogers, however, uses both "I" and "we" in his formal evaluation report on pages 119 through 144, but limits the use of the singular "I" to moments when he is clearly making a personal observation.

Use the Active Voice

Which of these sentences would you prefer to write?

A. Carl Dunstan investigated the problem.

B. The problem was investigated by Carl Dunstan.

In reporting writing you should try to be as direct and as brief as possible without losing any information. Since both sentences contain the same information, your choice should be sentence A because it is shorter and more direct.

Sentence A is written in the "active voice," in which the person or object performing the action is stated first, as follows:

Carl investigated the problem.
The shaft penetrated the casing.
Petra is studying the charts.

Sentence B is written in the "passive voice," in which the person or object performing the action is stated *after* the verb; for example:

The problem was investigated *by Carl.*
The casing was penetrated *by the shaft.*
The charts are being studied *by Petra.*

Sentences written in the active voice are generally shorter and more emphatic than sentences written in the passive voice. Similarly, reports written primarily in the active voice seem much stronger, more definite, and more convincing than reports written predominantly in the passive voice. Compare the following two paragraphs, both describing the same situation:

Primarily Passive Voice:

A study of electricity costs was conducted in three stages over a twelve-month period. First, a survey was taken and a list made of all apartment dwellers in the area. Then a table was constructed in which family size was compared against apartment size. Finally, an analysis was made of apartment dwellers' lifestyles and their major appliance ownership (it was assumed that a stove, refrigerator, and air-conditioner were installed as standard equipment in each apartment). *(75 unassertive words.)*

Primarily Active Voice:

We studied electricity costs in three stages over a twelve-month period. First we surveyed and listed all apartment dwellers in the area, and then constructed a chart comparing family size against apartment size. Finally we analyzed apartment dwellers' lifestyles and their major appliance ownership (we assumed that each apartment was equipped with a stove, refrigerator and air-conditioner as standard equipment). *(61 confident words.)*

The information conveyed by the two paragraphs is essentially the same, yet the impact each creates is markedly different. The active voice paragraph seems to be written by a confident, knowledgeable individual who uses the first person ("we") and clearly identifies that someone has been actively doing something. The passive voice paragraph seems to be written by someone who is detached and uninvolved; its author does not write in the first person, and so writes sentences without mentioning who performed the action. This creates the impression that he or she is merely passing along information.

Writing in the first person can help you avoid writing in the passive voice. When you write "I" or "we," you immediately identify who was involved:

I requested approval to visit...
Early in May *we* established criteria...

This becomes particularly important when you have to make recommendations. The Recommendations section of a report must be strong and
definite; yet often report writers adopt an indefinite, passive stance, writing

It is recommended that...

Instead, they should be firm and assertive, and write in the active voice:

I recommend...	(when the report writer is making a recommen- dation as an individual), or
We recommend...	(when he or she is making a recommendation on behalf of a group of people, the department, or the company).

Tod Phillips and Guy Desrogers both write "We recommend..." in the
Recommendations sections of their reports (see pages 77 and 141), while
Lorraine Dychuk writes "I recommend..." in her proposal on page 99.

Writing in the active voice does not mean you always have to write in
the first person. You can just as easily name another person, a department, or an object.

Mr Singh revised the estimate.
To meet the mailing deadline *the project group* worked until 3 a.m.
My bank increased the interest rate.
On the fourth floor *the mail cart* lost a wheel.
Our comptroller recommended a budget cut.
After reading our report, *the client* requested a revision.

Of course, when you do not know who performed the action, prefer
not to name names, or want to deemphasize the doer, then the passive
voice has to be used.

Your budget has been cut by 30%. *(Specific person not stated).*
The documents were misfiled. *(Person not known).*
The long-awaited Manston report has been printed. *(The emphasis
would be wrong in the active voice: "The printer has printed the long-
awaited Manston report").*

This section only draws your attention to the active voice and suggests
you use it wherever possible in your reports. For a more detailed description refer to a language textbook, such as *The Canadian Writer's
Handbook*.[3]

Avoid "Clutter"

The words you use in a report can do much to help your readers understand quickly what you have to say, and then react or respond in the way you want them to. A clear, concise report will evoke the correct reader response, but a report cluttered with unnecessary words and expressions can so muffle the message that readers either miss the point or lose interest and stop reading. Because "clutter" words are used frequently by *other* people, we tend to recognize them as old friends and so may have difficulty weeding them out of our own writing.

Use Simple Words

When you have the choice between two or more words, try using the simpler word. The accountant who refers to "remuneration" and "superannuation scheme" in an annual report would do better to write about pay, salary or wages, and the pension plan. Then he or she would be understood by virtually every reader, from the chief executive to the newly employed warehouseperson.

There are certain words peculiar to each of our particular vocations which we have to use because no other words can adequately replace them (computer specialists, for example, refer to "disks," "disk drives," and "bits" and "bytes" of information). To keep their sentences and paragraphs as uncluttered as possible, specialists should surround these technical words with mainly simple words.

Compare the following two sentences:

    A. An aberration of considerable magnitude significantly influenced the character readout.

    B. A large deviation seriously affected the character readout.

Readers would need a very good vocabulary to understand all the words in the first sentence, and even then they would have to read carefully to fully grasp what is being said. Most readers would understand the second sentence.

Remove Words of Low Information Content

If you want your writing to create a positive, purposeful impact, you cannot afford to insert words and expressions which neither clarify nor contribute to the message. Such words are known as "low information content"

(LIC) words, because they detract from rather than improve the message's clarity. There are several in the following sentence:

> In order to effect an improvement in package handling an effort should be made to move the shipping department so that it is located in the vicinity of the loading dock.

Can you identify the LIC words?

> *In order to* (replace with *to*)
> *effect an improvement in* (use *improve*)
> *an effort should be made* (replace with *we should*)
> *located in the vicinity of* (use *near*)

Without the LIC words the sentence reads

> To improve package handling we should move the shipping department so that it is near the loading dock.

Or (better still),

> To improve package handling we should move the shipping department nearer to the loading dock.

LIC words make writing seem woolly and indefinite. They flow easily from our pens and pencils, but once they are on paper they can be hard to identify. For example:

When we have written	*It can be difficult to think of*
brings to a conclusion	concludes
for a period of	during
it will be necessary to	we must
in the direction of	toward

Simply being aware that you should not use LIC words in your reports will help you to be a careful writer, but still will not prevent you from inserting them inadvertently during an enthusiastic burst of writing. After you have written your first draft, but before the final copy is typed, always take a few minutes to check that you have not used any unnecessary words. Some common LIC words and expressions are listed in Table 10-1.

Table 10-1
Some Typical Low Information Content (LIC)
Words and Expressions

These LIC words and phrases should be eliminated (indicated by X) or written in a shorter form (shown in brackets).

actually (X)
a majority of (most)
a number of (many, several)
as a means of (for, to)
as a result (so)
as necessary (X)
at present (X)
at the rate of (at)
at the same time as (while)
at this time (X)
bring to a conclusion (conclude)
by means of (by)
by the use of (by)
communicate with (talk to, telephone, write to)
connected together (connected)
contact (talk to, telephone, write to)
due to the fact that (because)
during the course of (during)
during the time that (while)
end result (result)
exhibit a tendency to (tend to)
for a period of (for)
for the purpose of (for, to)
for the reason that, for this reason (because)
in all probability (probably)
in an area where (where)
in an effort to (to)
in close proximity to (close to, near)
in colour, in length, in number, in size (X)

in connection with (about)
in fact, in point of fact (X)
in order to (to)
in such a manner as to (to)
in terms of (in, for)
in the course of (during)
in the direction of (toward)
in the event that (if)
in the form of (as)
in the light of (X)
in the neighbourhood of, in the vicinity of (about, approximately, near)
involves the use of (employs, uses)
involve the necessity of (demand, require)
is a person who (X)
is designed to be (is)
it can be seen that (thus, so)
it is considered desirable (I or we want to)
it will be necessary to (I, you, or we must)
of considerable magnitude (large)
on account of (because)
on the part of (X)
previous to, prior to (before)
subsequent to (after)
with the aid of (with)
with the result that (so, therefore)

Eliminate Overworked Expressions

Overworked expressions can create an even more noticeable negative effect than LIC words because they make their writer seem wordy or insincere, and sometimes pompous or evasive. Some typical expressions are listed in Table 10-2. These should be searched for, identified, and eliminated at the same time as you check for LIC words.

Table 10-2
Typical Overworked Expressions and Clichés

a matter of concern	in the long run
and/or	in the matter of
all things being equal	it stands to reason
as a last resort	last but not least
as a matter of fact	many and diverse
as per	needless to say
attached hereto	on the right track
at this point in time	par for the course
by no means	please feel free to
conspicuous by its absence	pursuant to your request
easier said than done	regarding the matter of
enclosed herewith	slowly but surely
for your information (as an introductory phrase)	this will acknowledge
	we are pleased to advise
if and when	we wish to state
in reference to	with reference to
in short supply	you are hereby advised
in the foreseeable future	

References

1 Ron S. Blicq, *Technically-Write! Communicating in a Technological Era*, Canadian 3rd Edn (Scarborough, Ont: Prentice-Hall Canada Inc., 1987), p. 190.

2 Ron S. Blicq, *Administratively-Write! Communicating in a Business Environment* (Scarborough, Ont: Prentice-Hall Canada Inc., 1985), p. 7.

3 William E. Messenger and Jan de Bruyn, *Canadian Writer's Handbook*, 2nd Edn (Scarborough, Ont: Prentice-Hall Canada Inc., 1986).

11

Writing a List of References or a Bibliography

Whenever you quote someone else's facts and figures, or draw information from a textbook, journal article, report, letter, or even a conversation, it is customary to acknowledge the source of your information within your report. This is usually done at the end of the report, in a section called "References" (or "List of References"), as Guy Desrogers has done in his formal report in chapter 8. References normally occur in longer reports and proposals—seldom in very short reports.

The purpose of a reference is threefold:

- To give your report credibility. (When readers encounter a statement such as, "A previous study has shown that 26% of the city's core area adults are unemployed," they expect to be told who made the original statement, and in what document it appeared.)
- To help readers refer to the same source, if they want more information.
- To give credit to the originator.

There are specific rules for writing a list of references, and to some extent they vary depending on what form your report is to be published in. The rules shown here are generally acceptable for any business or industry report. (But if, for example, your report is to appear in the journal of a professional society, then you should follow the style used by that journal. I am assuming that most reports you write will be issued by your company or organization, and that a standard style will be most applicable.)

How to Write References

References are listed in the order in which they appear in the report. If the first statement that needs to be supported concerns the quantity of water consumed by your city, then the first item in your list of references will be the document in which water consumption is tabulated. Each reference entry is numbered sequentially, starting at "1," and a corresponding number is shown in the report narrative to direct the reader's attention to the appropriate entry in the list of references. For example:

> Over the past eight years the city's water consumption has ranged from a low of 207 389 kilolitres per day to a high of 253 461 kilolitres.[1]
>
> *(This "1" refers to the first entry in the list of references.)*

Since every entry is numbered, a corresponding number like this must appear in the report narrative for each reference. (See Guy Desrogers' report, pages 129 and 133.)

Each entry in the list of references must supply certain primary information, so that the reader can clearly identify the document and be able to refer to it or order it. For example, the report must identify:

- who made the statement,
- in what document it appeared, or where and to whom it was said (if a spoken reference), and
- when the statement was made.

Every detail (such as the author's name and document title) must be copied *exactly* as it appears on the original document, so that readers will experience no difficulty in finding or ordering the document.

The preferred methods for listing the more common documents and conversations are described below.

Book by One Author.   The entry should contain

> author's name
> book title (underlined)
> city of publication
> name of publisher   } *(enclosed within brackets)*
> date of publication
> page number of specific reference (if applicable).

This book and page are an example:

1. Ron S. Blicq, Guidelines for Report Writing, 2nd Edn (Scarborough, Ont: Prentice-Hall Canada Inc., 1990), p. 171.

(*Note*: The edition number is omitted for the first edition of a book.)

Book by Two Authors.   Both authors are named; all other information is the same as for a single-author book.

2. William E. Messenger and Jan de Bruyn, The Canadian Writer's Handbook, 2nd Edn (Scarborough, Ont: Prentice-Hall Canada Inc., 1986), p. 370.

Book by Three or More Authors.   Only the primary author is named (usually the first-named author); remaining authors are replaced by the expression ''and others.'' All other information is the same as for a single-author book.

3. Donald L. MacRae and others, You and Others: An Introduction to Interpersonal Communication (Toronto, Ont: McGraw-Hill Ryerson Limited, 1975), p.57.

An Anthology. (a book containing sections written by different authors, with the whole book edited by another person). If your reference is to the whole book the editor's name is used and his or her editorial role is identified by the word ''ed'' immediately after the name.

4. Christine L. Summakindt, ed, Marketing in Pacific Rim Countries (Vancouver, BC: Dover Books Inc., 1990), p. 3.

If your reference is only to an article or section in the book, the author's name and section title are used, so that the entry contains

author's name (or authors' names)
section title (in quotation marks)
book title (underlined)
editor's name (if the book has an editor)
city of publication
name of publisher   ⎱ (*enclosed within brackets*)
date of publication   ⎰
page number on which article begins, or of specific reference

For example:

> 5. Jonathan Ng, "Interpersonal Communication with Asian Business-people," <u>Marketing in Pacific Rim Countries</u>, ed Christine L. Summakindt (Vancouver, BC: Dover Books Inc., 1990), p. 268.

Second or Third Edition of a Book.   If a book is a second or subsequent edition, the words "2nd Edn" (or 3rd, etc) should be entered immediately after the book title, as has been done in entries 1 and 2.

Article in a Magazine or Journal.   The entry should contain

> author's name (or authors' names)
> title of article (in quotation marks)
> title of magazine or journal (underlined)
> volume and issue numbers (shown as numerals only, e.g. 17:4)
> magazine or journal date
> page number on which article starts, or of specific reference

For example:

> 6. Dana Winterton, "Entrepreneurs in a Free Trade Environment," <u>Business–North</u>, 14:2, February 1989, p. 27.

If the author of a magazine article is not identified, the reference should start with the article title.

Report Written by Yourself or Another Person.   The entry should include

> author's name, or authors' names (if authors are identified)
> title of report (underlined)
> report number or identification (if applicable)
> name and location of organization issuing report
> date of report
> specific page number (if applicable)

Here is an entry for the formal business report in chapter 8:

> 7. Guy Desrogers, <u>Evaluation of Facsimile Transmission (FAX) for Use in Small Business Operations</u>. Report No. 90/1, Assiniboine Business Consultants Ltd., Winnipeg, Manitoba, January 12, 1990.

Technical Paper Presented at a Conference.   The entry should contain
author's name (or authors' names)
title of paper
name of conference and sponsoring organization
location of conference
date of presentation

For example:

8. Marvin Kreston, <u>Who Should Teach Business Managers How to Communicate?</u> Conference on Integrating Business and Education Communication Needs, Winnipeg, Man., November 18, 1989.

Letter or Correspondence.   The entry should have
author's name
author's identification (employer and location)
form of correspondence (letter, memorandum, telegram)
addressee's identification (employer and location)
date of letter

For example:

9. Maurice Aubert, Meridian Laboratories, Montreal, Que. Letter to Ken Fong, Vancourt Business Systems Inc., Winnipeg, Man., January 22, 1990.

Speech or Conversation.   The entry should be
speaker's name
speaker's identification (employer and location)
form of communication (speech, conversation, telephone call)
listener's name (individual or group)
listener's identification (employer and/or location)
date of communication

For example:

10. Lloyd R. McGinnis, Wardrop Engineering Inc., Winnipeg, Man., speaking to the IEEE International Professional Communication Conference, Winnipeg, Man., October 14, 1987.

11. Helen M. Ainslie, Western Supplies Ltd., Vancouver, BC, in conversation with Douglas G. Jerome, NOR-ED Distributors, Edmonton, Alberta, December 13, 1989.

Second Reference to a Document.   When a document is referred to more than once, an abbreviated reference containing only the author's surname (or authors' surnames) and new page number can be used for all subsequent entries. If, for example, further references are made to the documents listed earlier as entries 2 and 6, the new entries would be

12. Messenger and de Bruyn, p.126.

13. Winterton, p. 31.

(Note that the Latin terms *ibid.* and *op. cit.* are not used in modern reports.) If several documents by the same author are referenced, then the date of publication is included in subsequent entries (to identify which of the author's specific works is being referred to):

14. Carter, 1989, p. 147.

Bibliographies and Footnotes

A bibliography is used when a report writer wants to list more documents than are referred to in the report. It may be a comprehensive list of all documents pertaining to the topic being discussed, or it may be limited to the sources that were used to research and conduct the project or study.

The information in a bibliography is almost identical to the information in a list of references, but the entries are presented differently. In bibliography entries the following rules apply:

- The first-named author's names are reversed, with the surname shown first and the first names shown second (for example, Messenger, William E.) Second authors' names are listed in natural order (Messenger, William E. and Jan de Bruyn).
- The first line of each entry is extended about 13 millimetres or five typewriter spaces to the left of all other lines in the entry.
- The entries are listed in alphabetical order of first-named authors, so that Ainslie appears before Desrogers, who appears before Winterton.
- The entries are not preceded by an identification number.
- Within each entry the information is most often divided into three compartments, which are separated by periods:

    Author identification.
    Document or article title.
    Publisher identification.

For example:

> Smithers, Janet and William Corcoran. "Fund Raising for The Arts."
> Canadian Financial News, 27:15, June 17, 1988.

The documents listed earlier as references are shown rearranged into a bibliography in Figure 11-1. Like a list of references, a bibliography appears at the end of the report narrative, but before the attachments or appendices.

```
                           BIBLIOGRAPHY


     Ainslie, Helen M., Western Supplies Ltd., Vancouver,
          BC. Conversation with Douglas G. Jerome, NOR-ED
          Distributors, Edmonton, Alta, December 13, 1989.

     Aubert, Maurice, Meridian Laboratories, Montreal, Que.
          Letter to Ken Fong, Vancourt Business Systems
          Inc., Winnipeg, Man., January 22, 1990.

     Blicq, Ron S. Guidelines for Report Writing, 2nd Edn.
          Scarborough, Ont: Prentice-Hall Canada Inc., 1990.

     Desrogers, Guy. Evaluation of Facsimile Transmission
          (FAX) For Use in Small Business Operations.
          Report No. 90/1, Assiniboine Business Consultants
          Ltd., Winnipeg, Man., January 12, 1990.

     Kreston, Marvin. Who Should Teach Business Managers
          How to Communicate? Conference on Integrating
          Business and Education Communication Needs,
          Winnipeg, Man., November 18, 1989.

     MacRae, Donald L., and others. You and Others: An
          Introduction to Interpersonal Communication.
          Toronto, Ont: McGraw-Hill Ryerson Limited, 1975.

     McGinnis, Lloyd R., Wardrop Engineering Inc., Winnipeg,
          Man. Speech to the IEEE International Profes-
          sional Communication Conference, Winnipeg, Man.,
          October 14, 1987.

     Messenger, William E., and Jan de Bruyn. The Canadian
          Writer's Handbook, 2nd Edn. Scarborough, Ont:
          Prentice-Hall Canada Inc., 1986.

     Summakindt, Christine L., ed. Marketing in Pacific Rim
          Countries. Vancouver, BC: Dover Books Inc., 1990.

     Winterton, Dana. "Entrepreneurs in a Free Trade
          Environment." Business--North, 14:2, February
          1989.
```

Fig. 11-1. *A bibliography.*

Note that there is no reference to the Jonathan Ng article in the bibliography, since there is already a reference to the anthology in which the article appeared (under the name of the editor, Christine L. Summakindt). If the anthology had not been included, then the article would have been entered and would have appeared like this:

Ng, Jonathan. "Interpersonal Communication with Asian Business-people." <u>Marketing in Pacific Rim Countries</u>, ed Christine L. Summakindt. Vancouver, BC: Dover Books Inc., 1990.

Footnotes are not recommended for business and technical reports. Their position at the foot of the page not only distracts the reader's eye and interrupts reading continuity, but also creates difficulties for the person typing the report. Footnotes are better replaced by endnotes (that is, a list of references at the end of the report), which much more conveniently and unobtrusively serve the same purpose.

12

Inserting Illustrations into Reports

An illustration can help readers understand more readily a difficult part of a report, or a particular point a report writer wants to make. Because its role is to enhance rather than duplicate the narrative, an illustration must be simple, clear, and useful. A reader should not have to turn to the report's words to understand an illustration.

Illustrations appear mostly in longer, more formal reports, such as analyses, feasibility studies, proposals, and investigation or evaluation reports.

Before inserting an illustration a report writer should ask three questions:

1. Which kind of illustration (e.g. a table, graph, bar chart, flow diagram, photograph, etc) will best illustrate a particular feature or characteristic?

2. Will readers be using the illustration simply to gain a visual impression of an aspect being discussed, or will they be expected to extract information from it?

3. Will the illustration be referred to only once, to amplify or explain a point, or will it be referred to several times in the report narrative? (If it will be referred to frequently, its position becomes important.)

Every illustration should be numbered sequentially, so that it can be easily referred to in the report narrative.

> ...in figure 2 the monthly profits for financial year 1989-90 are compared with those for the two previous years.

The illustration should also have a title.

> Fig. 2.   Financial year 1989-90 profits compared to two previous years.

Sometimes a caption follows the title, to draw attention to an important point or explain some aspect in more detail. For example (continuing from the figure 2 title):

> Both curves for previous years show a distinct flattening about six months before the profits reach their lowest level. This flattening is not evident in the 1989-90 curve.

Report writers must also decide whether an illustration should be placed directly in or beside the report narrative, or as an attachment or appendix at the end of the report. For example:

- If the illustration is extremely complex or fills more than one page, it should be an attachment.
- If readers will need to refer to the illustration as they read the report, it should be placed in the report narrative.
- If an illustration meets both the previous criteria, then the complete illustration should be an attachment, and a smaller, much less detailed illustration should be prepared and inserted into the report proper.

Tables

Tables document information in tabular form, such as results of tests, quantities of items manufactured, daily receipts, etc. Unlike many of the illustrations described in this chapter, tables are meant to be examined in detail by the reader, who may want to extract or extrapolate data from them. Consequently, the rules for preparing tables differ from the rules for preparing illustrations such as graphs and charts.

Guidelines for preparing tables are:

1. Keep the table simple, using as few columns as possible.
2. Limit the amount of data by omitting any details readers will not need.
3. Insert a clear, simple, but fully understandable title at the head of each column.

4. Insert a unit of measurement at the head of a column, rather than repeating the unit after each entry within the column. (See how this has been done for "km/hr" and "$" in the table in Figure 12-1.)

5. Insert the table number and an informative title, and centre them either immediately above or below the table (above the table is preferred—see Figure 12-1).

6. Decide whether the table is to be "open" (without ruled lines separating the columns, as in Figure 12-1), or "closed" (with the ruled lines inserted, as on page 97).

The narrative part of the report should inform readers what they should learn from the table, so that its relevance is clear.

TABLE 2 Speeding Infractions by Employees Operating Company Vehicles					
January 1 to March 31, 1989					
Date of Offence	*Driver*	*Vehicle (Lic. No.)*	*Speed Recorded (km/hr)*	*Speed in Excess of Limit (km/hr)*	*Fine ($)*
Jan 17	B. Bastian*	JGR 611	101	36	81.00
Feb 04	K. Meursault	JGR 608	66	26	66.50
Feb 04	M. Fong	MND 147	61	11	38.50
Feb 19	R. Kurilicki	JGR 608	68	28	51.00
Mar 02	B. Bastian*	JGR 611	123	63	135.00
Mar 15	K. Fallis	MND 176	67	27	67.50
Mar 21	R. Ingraham	JGR 609	94	29	70.00
*Employment terminated March 31.					

Fig. 12-1. *An "open" table (no lines separate the columns of data).*

Graphs

Graphs offer a simple way to illustrate how one factor affects, or is affected by, another. They have the particular advantage that, providing they are not too complex, the changes they depict can be readily visualized and understood by most readers. For example, graphs can be used to show:

• Predicted sales for varying price structures.

• The increase in fuel consumption resulting from increased highway speeds.

- Personal life expectancy in relation to the quantity of cigarettes smoked.
- Weight reduction in relation to lower calorie intakes.

No matter how "technical" the subject illustrated, graphs must be kept simple: their purpose is to enhance the reader's understanding of the report. The guidelines listed here all contribute to this cardinal rule.

1. Limit the number of curves on a graph to three if the curves cross one another, or four if they do not intersect or there is only a simple intersection. If you have to construct a multiple-curve graph containing five or more curves, construct two graphs rather than one.

2. Differentiate between curves, particularly if they intersect, by assigning them different "weights." Make the most important curve a bold line, the next most important a light line, the third curve a series of dashes, and the least important curve a series of dots (see Figure 12-2). Avoid the temptation to use colours to differentiate between curves, because all the colours will print black on any copies made with an office copier.

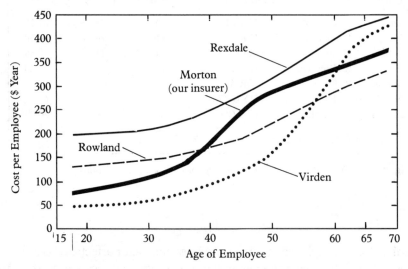

COMPARATIVE COSTS OF FOUR EMPLOYEE INSURANCE PLANS

Fig. 12-2. *A graph with four curves. The most important curve is identified by a bold line.*

3. Position the curves so they are reasonably centred within the frame provided by the graph's axes. If necessary adjust the starting point of

the scale(s) to move an off-centred curve to a more central position. See Figures 12-3 and 12-4.

4. Select a scale interval for each axis which will help the curves create a visually accurate image (Figure 12-5). An incorrect scale interval may inadvertently cause curves to depict a false impression, as shown in Figure 12-6.

5. Omit all plot points, to provide a clean, uncluttered illustration. The only time that plot points or lines should be present is in a detailed drawing placed in an attachment, from which readers are expected to extract information or examine the graph's construction.

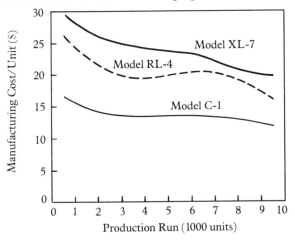

Fig. 12-3. *An incorrectly centred graph. Although tech nically accurate, the graph appears unbalanced.*

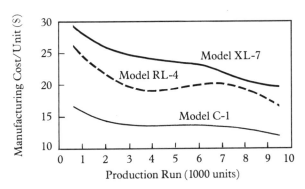

Fig. 12-4. *A correctly centred graph. The vertical scale starts at 10 rather than at 0 as in Fig. 12-3.*

6. Keep all lettering clear, brief, and *horizontal*. The only non-horizontal lettering should be along the vertical axis, as shown in Figures 12-2 to 12-5. Particularly avoid placing lettering along the slope of a curve.

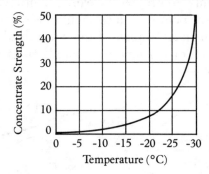

Fig. 12-5. *Properly balanced scale intervals produce a visually accurate curve.*

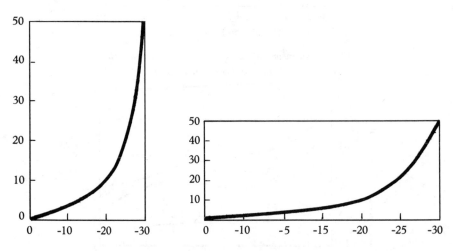

Fig. 12-6. *The effect of an improperly balanced scale interval. Although these curves are technically accurate, neither creates the same visual impression as the correctly balanced curve in Fig. 12-5. The contracted axes overaccentuate the flattening at one end, and deemphasize the flattening at the other end of each curve.*

7. Omit a grid unless you expect your readers will want to extract their own figures from the graph (compare the no-grid graph in Figure 12-4 with the gridded graph in Figure 12-5). If you are unsure whether to insert grid lines, you can insert an "implied" grid, as in Figure 12-2.

Bar Charts

Whereas graphs have two continuously variable functions, bar charts have only one. They are simpler to read and understand than graphs, and so are particularly useful as illustrations for non-specialist or "lay" readers. Normally they provide only a general indication of results, quantity, time, etc, which makes them unsuitable for depicting exact units of measurement; nor can readers extrapolate detailed or exact information from them.

A bar chart offers comparisons, using parallel bars of varying lengths to portray weight, growth, cost, life expectancy, etc, of various items. The bars are arranged either vertically or horizontally, depending on the factors being displayed, with the variable function lying along the axis which runs parallel to the bars.

General guidelines for preparing bar charts are:

1. Position the bars so they are spaced one bar-width apart.

2. Arrange the bars vertically when you are portraying "growth" factors, such as weight, quantity, cost, or units produced (see Figure 12-7).

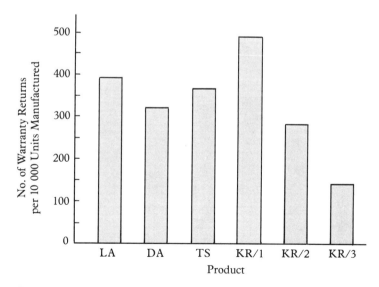

Fig. 12-7. *A bar chart with vertical bars.*

3. Arrange the bars horizontally when you are portraying elapsed time, or factors in which time is a significant element (i.e. life expectancy, production time, project length), as shown in Figure 12-8).

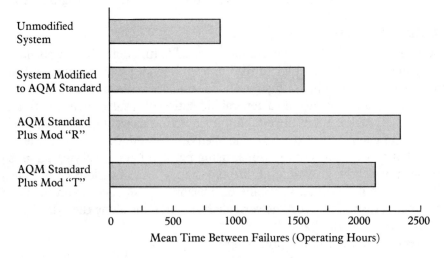

Fig. 12-8.   *A bar chart with horizontal bars.*

4. Shade the bars if you need to make them stand out.
5. If it is important for readers to know the exact total each bar represents, show the totals either immediately above the tops of the bars (if the figures are short enough), or inside the bars (along their length), as shown in Figure 12-9.

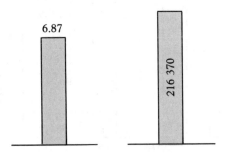

Fig. 12-9.   *Numbers placed above or within bars show exact figures.*

6. If the bars are composed of several segments, either identify the segments by various types of shading (and provide a legend beside or below
   the chart) or, if there is room, identify each segment with a word or
   two inside the bars (see Figure 12-10).

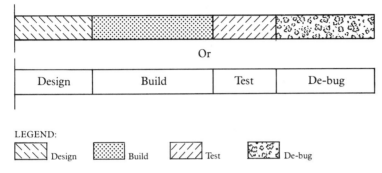

Fig. 12-10.   *Bars can be divided into segments either by shading or lettering.*

An unusual illustrative technique is to use pictorial bars, inserting a picture of a car, person, building, etc, the size or height of which provides
the comparison (see Figure 12-11). This technique is seen more often in
magazines and newspapers than in business reports.

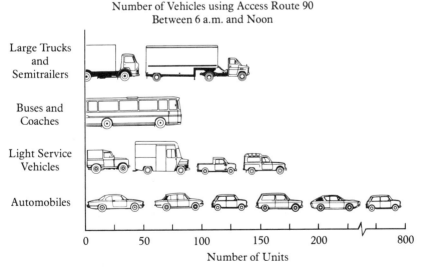

Fig. 12-11.   *A pictorial bar chart. The horizontal axis is broken and shortened between
225 and 775 to permit the long Automobiles bar to be depicted without unbalancing the
illustration.*

Histograms

A histogram contains some features common to both a graph and a bar chart. It has two continuously variable functions, but is constructed like a bar chart because there is insufficient data on which to plot a true curve. To show that it has this dual but limited function, the bars are plotted immediately against each other as in Figure 12-12. Indeed, a line drawn through the tops of the bars would produce a rudimentary curve.

Guidelines for preparing a histogram are similar to those applicable to preparing a graph and a bar chart.

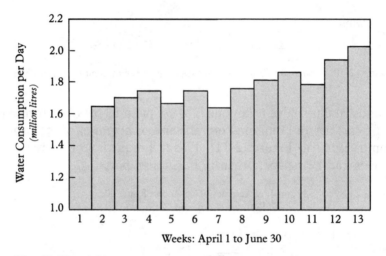

Fig. 12-12.   *A histogram.*

Surface Charts

An illustration which combines the characteristics of both a graph and a histogram is the surface chart. It has two continuous variables, and it is made up of adjoining bars from which the vertical construction lines have been erased (see Figure 12-13). But the curves, instead of being compared as in a graph, are summated; that is, for each vertical "bar," the factors being displayed are added, so that the first curve *becomes the base* for the second curve, and the second curve *becomes the base* for the third curve. Thus the uppermost curve represents the total of all the curves added together.

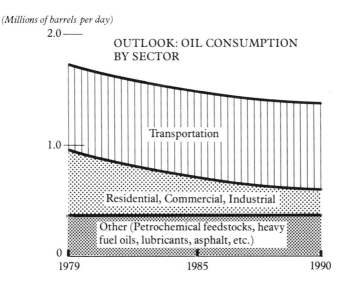

Fig. 12-13. *A surface chart.*

Readers cannot easily extrapolate information from surface charts because direct readings can be extracted only from the lowest and uppermost curves.

Guidelines for preparing a surface chart are:

1. For the lowest curve, choose and draw in the factor which is the most important, represents the largest quantity to be depicted, or offers the most stable (even) curve ("Other" in Figure 12-13).

2. For the second curve, select the next factor and plot it in, using the first curve as the base for each section ("Residential" in Figure 12-13).

3. Repeat the sequence for each additional curve ("Transportation" in Figure 12-13).

4. Shade or cross-hatch the curves, preferably making the lowest section the darkest and the uppermost section the lightest.

Pie Charts

A pie chart (Figure 12-14) is one of the simplest forms of illustration. By dividing a circle (a "pie") into segments of varying size, we can illustrate such things as market distributions, tax apportionment, and product costs in a readily understandable form. Because it is a simple illustration, only a few guidelines are necessary:

1. Always make the segments of a pie chart add up to an exact "1," 100%, or $1.00 (or a round figure multiple: $100, $1 million).
2. Check that the segments are visually accurate; i.e. that they are in the correct proportions for the quantities they depict.
3. If there are a lot of very small segments to depict, combine them into one segment and label it "Miscellaneous" (or use a more descriptive term). If it is important for readers to know the composition of this segment, provide a list beside the illustration or in a caption below the chart.

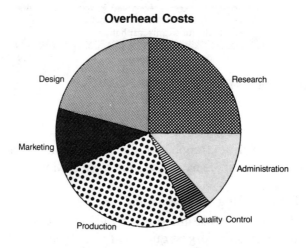

Overhead Costs

Distribution by Departments

Fig. 12-14. *A pie chart.*

Flow Charts, Site Plans and Line Diagrams

A flow chart (see Figure 12-15) provides a visual description of a procedure, process, plan or system. A site plan depicts the more significant features of a building site or small area of a town, while a line diagram can encompass anything which needs to be illustrated (e.g. a piece of equipment, hook-up of several instruments, layout of an office, etc). In all cases they should:

• be as simple as possible,

• clarify the accompanying written description,

- contain only the essential elements (which means firmly eliminating unessential elements),
- be easy to follow,
- be readily understood without the written description,
- be drawn in clear black ink, and
- contain neatly lettered, clear but brief explanatory words.

Preparing a Proposal (Pre-Writing Steps)

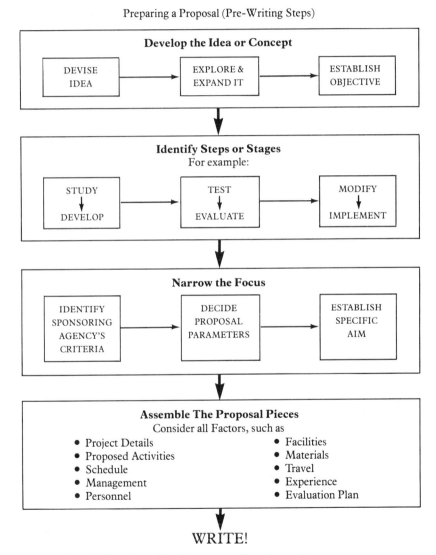

Fig. 12-15. *A flow chart (also known as a flow diagram).*

Photographs

Photographs are an ideal, accurate way to show readers either close-up details or "the whole picture," but unfortunately they are awkward and expensive to reproduce. Consequently report writers have to consider whether the time and cost of reproducing photographs is justified, or if the same information can be conveyed just as easily and more economically by inserting a sketch or line drawing into a report.

The chief problem with photographs is that the average office copier does not reproduce them well. To achieve a fine quality image, photographs have to be carefully prepared for printing by a lithographer, who places a fine dot-screen over them and makes a special plate for printing them onto bond paper with an offset duplicator. As few businesses have the facilities to do all of this in-house, the work usually has to be subcontracted. This can be inconvenient and costly unless a large number of copies of the report are to be printed.

If only a very few copies are to be made of a report, photographic prints can be inserted manually in several ways.

1. If there are several prints and they are small, they may be glued into the report in spaces left open for them during typing.

2. If there are only one or two prints and they are large (8 × 10 in.), they may be glued onto a full-size page on which a title and caption have been pretyped.

3. If there are several medium or large prints, they may be inserted into a prepared pocket or sleeve (an envelope with one end snipped off is ideal), which has been mounted on a piece of card. The pocket is placed at the back of the report and preceded by a sheet listing the photographs. Each photograph should be coded on the front for identification, and cross-referenced to this list.

Remember that photographs are bulky and tend to curl. If there are too many of them they can create an uneven, awkward looking document, in which case you may prefer to bind them into a separate folder which accompanies your report.

The Size and Position of Illustrations

The ideal illustration sits beside or immediately above or below the words which refer to it. Unfortunately this convenient juxtaposition is not always easy to achieve, particularly if a report is to be printed on only one side of the paper. If full-page tables and illustrations are inserted into the narrative, they completely interrupt reading continuity.

Use these guidelines when preparing a report for typing:

1. Plan the report's pages before they are typed or keystroked in their final form, even if doing so means having an intermediary draft typed so that you can evaluate how much space each paragraph will require.

2. Keep diagrams as simple as possible, and as small as possible, so there will be room to insert type above or below them.

3. Position diagrams so they are adjacent to the paragraphs which refer to them or to paragraphs which most need illustrative support.

4. Beneath every illustration insert the figure number, a brief title and, possibly, an explanatory caption (see how this has been done in Figure 12-16).

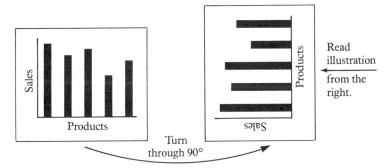

Fig. 12-16.   *Full-page horizontal diagrams are turned so they can be read from the right. This should be done even though some words may be inverted when the illustration is viewed from the foot of the page.*

5. If a full-page diagram has to be inserted, consider whether it must accompany the report narrative, or can be placed in an attachment with a small, simple sketch inserted in its place in the body of the report.

6. If a full-page diagram is horizontally oriented (i.e. its base is longer than its height), turn it through 90° so that it will be read from the right-hand side of the page. (See Figure 12-16, and the horizontally-oriented table on page 101).

7. Check that every illustration is referred to in the report narrative, either by its figure number or by its attachment identification.

13

Guidelines for Spelling and Handling Abbreviations and Numbers

Most publishers have a style manual which establishes rules for spelling, capitalization, writing numbers, and so on. Publishers, writers and editors refer to the style manual as their "bible," and use it whenever a decision on style is necessary (e.g. when they need to know if they should write "twelve" or "12," "km/hr" or "km/h," "analysed" or "analyzed"). Individual report writers do not have a special style manual to refer to, but they can adopt some of the basic guidelines which are common to most style manuals. These fundamental rules, and some additional suggestions, are outlined here.

Spelling

Canadian report writers have a special problem with spelling. Should they adopt the traditional British-based rules for words such as *manoeuvre*, *centre*, and *programme*, or spell them the American way—*maneuver*, *center*, and *program*? The choice is yours, because there are few definitive guidelines.

If your correspondence and reports go almost entirely to Canadian readers, then you can safely spell the British way. But if your words will be read frequently by U.S. readers, then you would be wise to spell the American way. The important thing is to be consistent: decide which way you prefer to spell and then use that spelling for *all* letters and reports.

Depending on your choice of spelling style, select a dictionary published in Canada, Britain, or the U.S. which is large enough to carry most of the words you are likely to use (a 600-page dictionary is ideal), and which has been revised recently (say within the past five years) so that it reflects current spelling practice. Use this dictionary's spelling rules as *your* rules, so that you will be consistent. Where the dictionary shows alternatives, such as "centre; center" and "programed; programmed", generally choose the first-listed spelling because dictionarymakers normally list the preferred or more common spelling first. If you decide you prefer the alternative spelling, then underline it with a coloured pen so you will be reminded of your preference when you look up the word later. The need to identify an alternative spelling may seem rare, but there will be occasions when you feel that the first-listed spelling is awkward (for example, many people feel "programed" is an unnatural spelling, and choose to write "programmed").

Some useful books which list many "problem" words are: Rudolph Flesch's *Look it Up*[1]; The *Government Printing Office Style Manual*[2], which lists nearly 20 000 compound terms; and for business and technical report writers, *Administratively-Write!*[3] and *Technically-Write!*[4], which list many "awkward to handle" words and expressions in their glossaries.

Abbreviations

You may abbreviate any term you wish, particularly if it is a lengthy term which will be used frequently in a report. These are the guidelines you should adhere to:

1. Indicate to the reader what your abbreviation means by stating it fully the first time and then showing the abbreviated form in parentheses beside it.

   The digital reference number (drf) we applied to the first set...
   In the second set, the drf was determined by...

2. Avoid forming your own abbreviation when another abbreviation already exists and is commonly used.

3. Use lower case letters, unless the abbreviation is formed from a proper noun such as a person's name.

metre	m
average	ave
ampere	A (formed from Ampere)

4. Omit all punctuation, unless the abbreviated term forms another word.

number	no.
absolute	abs
approximately	approx

5. Omit the "s" from an abbreviation of a plural quantity.

metres	m
numbers	no.
kilograms	kg
hours	hr

Be aware that there are some exceptions to these guidelines, caused by nonstandard terms being adopted through general usage. For example, although "no." is the correct abbreviation for "number," you are much more likely to see it used as "No." (and sometimes even as "#," which is definitely nonstandard). You will not be wrong if you choose to use "No." but be consistent: whichever term you use, use it all the time.

Numbers

Publishers' style manuals also reflect standard usage for writing numbers when they appear as part of a sentence or paragraph. The general rule is from one to nine, spell the number. For 10 and higher, use numerals. But there are exceptions to this rule, and sometimes you may have to decide whether the rule or the exception takes precedence.

1. Spell out the number if it is:
   - the first word in a sentence,
   - a large generalization (as in "...about eight thousand..."), or
   - a fraction which is less than one (as in "...only one-third of the participants...").
2. Use numerals if the number:
   - is part of a series of quoted numbers,
   - is a year, date, time, age (of a person), percentage or sum of money,
   - is part of a unit of measurement (as in "28 grams"),
   - is specific technical data, such as a dimension, tolerance, temperature or result of a test,
   - contains a decimal or a fraction (as in "6½" and "3.25"), or
   - refers to a chapter, figure (illustration), page (as in "page 138"), etc.

Also, insert a "zero" at the start of any decimal which is less than "1" (as in "0.25" and "0.0056").

Metric (SI) Units

As metrication becomes more firmly established, report writers—and particularly those who write technical reports—have to know the rules for writing metric (SI) units. These were defined originally by the eleventh (1960) Conférence Générale des Poids et Mesures (CGPM) in Paris, France, and have been only slightly revised in the intervening years. In Canada they are interpreted by the Canadian Standards Association's "Canadian Metric Practice Guide" CAN3-Z234.1-76. The current guidelines for writing SI symbols are:

1. Use upright (*not italic*) type.
2. Use lower case letters, except when a symbol is derived from a person's name (as in "V" for volts," which is derived from Volta).
3. Insert a space between the numeral and the first letter of the symbol (as in "38 kHz"), but *no* space between the symbols themselves (e.g. there is no space between "k" and "Hz").
4. Omit the "s" from all plurals (as in "221 km"), but do not insert a period at the end of the symbol (except when the symbol is the last word in a sentence).
5. Insert an oblique stroke for the word "per" (as in "km/hr", and a dot at mid-letter height to show that two symbols are multiplied (as in "N·m", for "Newton meter").

More detailed instructions, plus numerous examples, are contained in the glossaries of *Administratively-Write!* and *Technically-Write!*, referenced below.

References

1 Rudolph Flesch, *Look it Up: A Deskbook of American Spelling and Style* (New York: Harper and Row, 1977).

2 *United States Government Printing Office Style Manual*, Superintendent of Documents, Washington, DC, 20402.

3 Ron S. Blicq, *Administratively-Write! Communicating in a Business Environment* (Scarborough, Ont: Prentice-Hall Canada Inc., 1985), p. 566.

4 Ron S. Blicq, *Technically-Write! Communicating in a Technological Era*, Canadian 3rd Edn (Scarborough, Ont: Prentice-Hall Canada Inc., 1987), p. 387.

14

Guidelines for Writing at a Computer Terminal

In previous chapters I have assumed that you are handwriting your letters and reports, having a draft typed by a secretary or someone in a typing pool, then editing your own work and having it retyped. However, this method of report writing is changing rapidly as more and more people in business, industry, and government use personal computers or have a computer terminal at their desks. Because a computer allows them to keystroke rather than handwrite their first drafts, and even to keystroke their own corrections (''keystroke'' is the word-processing term for ''type''), many people find it a much faster, more expedient way to write.

For readers who already keystroke their own letters and reports, or anticipate they soon will, this chapter provides guidelines for writing and editing at a computer terminal. It also takes a brief look at desktop publishing (DTP), the impact it is having on the preparation and production of a company's publications, and the effect it will likely have on report writers. (Bear in mind, however, that computer technology is advancing so rapidly that what is considered new technology today will shortly become commonplace, and in a year or two may be obsolete.)

Word Processing Systems

In the beginning there were two types of word processing systems. Some, such as Wang, were ''dedicated'' systems in that they were built solely to do word processing and—at least at first—were not really equipped to work as computers. Others, such as the IBM and Apple families, started solely as computers and then were equipped with WP (word-processing) software. At first the dedicated systems were much more powerful and easier to use for WP work. The computer systems were more complex because their early WP software required more keystrokes and had fewer function keys.

Since then, WP software has been greatly improved, so that today dedicated WP systems are seldom used as a business writer's tool other than in stenographic centres. For this chapter I will assume you are using WP software rather than a dedicated system.

Most people who keystroke their own work use WP software stored on a hard disk within a personal computer, or on a floppy diskette they insert into the computer's disk drive. Alternatively, they "access," or make use of, the WP software stored in the memory of a mainframe computer's central processing unit (CPU).

There are two basic types of WP software. In one, instructions for centring, underlining, boldfacing and sometimes for starting a new paragraph or page are keystroked directly into the work and appear on the screen as "embedded" commands. These commands are often one or two letters preceded by a dot or period, such as .op (for "omit page numbers") and .rm75 (for "set right margin at column 75"), and are known as *dot commands*. Their presence can make on-screen reading difficult because the user does not see *exactly* what he or she will get when the report is printed. (The dot commands appear only on screen; they are eliminated when the report is printed on paper as "hard copy.")

The other type of software is commonly known as WYSIWYG, which is pronounced "wizziwig" and means "What you see is what you get." With WYSIWYG, there are no embedded commands to insert, so the words on the screen appear exactly as they will appear when printed as hard copy. Some systems even show the work on the screen in the correct typeface. WYSIWYG software is simpler to use than software that requires the user to insert embedded commands, and so is more popular. However, it requires more computer memory.

Why Keystroke Your Own Work?

The transition from the traditional form of writing to the keyboard can be traumatic. Most of us are accustomed to letting our thoughts flow via a pen or pencil onto paper, so that the writing instrument in our hand becomes part of the creative process. For many people, facing a computer terminal perched above a keyboard can inhibit their writing at first: they feel that pressing keys to form words and sentences is too clinical, and being unable to glance back and see their sentences and paragraphs grow into familiar pages of narrative is both impersonal and inconvenient.

Yet there are significant advantages to keystroking your own work. The most important is time. If you key your own words into a computer, you can proofread them in two ways: as typed images on the screen, or as printed words on paper, obtained from a printer. You can also use the WP program's spell-checker to identify typographical and spelling errors (such programs are not infallible, as will be explained later, but they do automatically identify a good percentage of the more obvious errors without your having to search for them). If you subsequently make changes to the draft, you do not have to re-proofread any words that you have not changed, as you would if they had been retyped manually. You can also visualize how your work is being spaced as you type it—and make adjustments for diagrams as you go along—instead of having to wait until the draft comes back to see how the typist has interpreted your requirements.

Do you need to be an experienced typist to keystroke a report? The answer is "no," although being able to type will obviously speed up your work initially. There are many "two-finger" report writers who can keystroke their reports just as quickly and as accurately as colleagues who know how to type properly.

Some Word Processing Definitions

Throughout this chapter I will be using word processing (WP) terms that you may or may not be familiar with. Here are some brief definitions:

- **Boot up:** To boot up a system is to move into the basic operating system, such as MS/DOS. From the operating system you can move into a specific WP program, such as *Microsoft Word, Wordperfect,* or *Wordstar.*

- **Dedicated:** The word "dedicated" is used to define a system that is confined to single-purpose use.

- **Default:** This is an often-used term in computer operations, but one that is seldom defined. A "default" is a condition that the system will adopt automatically unless you give it alternative instructions (e.g. the system may have been programmed to insert page numbers automatically starting at page 1, unless you tell it either to omit page numbers or to start with a different number).

- **Hard Copy:** When computer information is printed onto paper, the print-out is referred to as "hard copy."

- **Justified:** In justified text the words (and sometimes individual letters) are spaced so that every full line ends at the same point along the page. Thus the lines form a "straight" vertical right-hand margin, just like the left-hand margin. (These pages are right-justified.)

- **Keystroke:** When you write on a typewriter, you type; when you write at a computer terminal, you keystroke, or "key in."

- **Save** (or **Save to file**): As you keystroke, the words are stored in a temporary file in the computer's central processing unit (CPU). At the end of a keystroking task, you have to transfer the words from the CPU to permanent storage on a hard or floppy disk. (This is known as "saving" one's data. If you forget to save your work before switching off the computer, with most systems your unsaved work is automatically lost from the CPU's memory.)

Developing an Outline

An outline is even more important when you keystroke a report than when you write with a pen or pencil, because you cannot see the report physically growing on the pages or look back quite as readily at what you have written, particularly if you are writing a long report. You need an outline—even a very rough one—to help you keep the shape and design of the report continually before you. You can prepare your outline on paper or you can keystroke it directly into the computer. The method described here is for keystroking; a similar method is used for handwriting an outline. (Some WP software includes a built-in outlining program such as *PC Outline* by Brown Bag Software. If your WP program has this feature, you may prefer to use it rather than the method described here.)

Step 1. Boot up the system and create a file called PRE-OUTL (for "preliminary outline"), or assign it a descriptive name of your own choice. Into this file keystroke a list of headings, double spaced one above the other, each describing a topic you feel should be covered in your report. For example:

Width of shaft

Elevator sizes

Problem with access

Initial failure (May)

Current limitations

      ...etc.

The key to preparing this list is *not* to organize it as you go along. Relax, place your fingers on the keyboard, and keystroke whatever topic comes to mind first. And then keystroke another...and another...and another. What you will be doing is "brainstorming" ideas into the computer. The sequence in which they appear, and their importance or even their relevance, should not be considered at this point. That will come later, when you start arranging the information into a coherent outline.

When you have exhausted all likely topics, save the file to disk and then call it back to your screen. Return to the start of the file and for each topic you listed ask yourself two questions:

• Is the topic really relevant?
• What subtopics does it generate?

If you decide a heading is interesting but not truly relevant, then delete it (remember that you will not have totally lost it if you later change your mind, because the complete list you keystroked is still stored unchanged on the disk). If the topic generates additional ideas, keystroke them into the file immediately after the topic entry, and indent them to the right to show they are subordinate topics:

Width of shaft
Elevator sizes
   Regular
   Freight
   Executive
Problem with access
   First evidence—November
   Comments—safety inspector
   Meeting—February
Initial failure (May)
     ...*etc.*

When you feel you have developed a comprehensive list of topics (even though they are in random order) print out a hard copy to work with.

Step 2.   You now have to take the random list and assign each topic to one of the writing compartments of the report. Turn to earlier chapters of this book and decide which type of report you will be writing. Find the pyramid illustration containing the writing plan for the report, and identify the writing compartment names. Give each a one-letter label, such as "I" for Introduction, "A" for Approach, "F" for Findings, and "C" for Conclusions. On the hard copy, write an appropriate one-letter label either in front of or behind every entry in the list. For example, after "Width of shaft" you might write "I" if you want to provide details of the shaft's size in the Introduction to your report, or "F" if you feel the width of the shaft is one of the report's Findings. (With experience you can also do this annotating on screen, without using hard copy, but it is more difficult because you cannot see all the items at once.)

Step 3.   Now you can form your writing outline. If you originally key-stroked the topics in a roughly coherent order—and this sometimes occurs because one topic often generates the next logical topic—you may be able to rearrange them on screen. More often, however, you will find that there are so many changes that it is faster to prepare a completely new list. In this case, either keystroke from your annotated hard copy or print out a hard copy with the writing compartment annotations on it.

Create a new file called OUTLINE and in capital letters keystroke the appropriate labels of the writing compartments into it, such as those for an investigation report (see Figure 6-1 on page 68), so that they appear as a series of main headings:

SUMMARY
INTRODUCTION
INVESTIGATION
   APPROACH
   FINDINGS
   SUGGESTIONS
   EVALUATION
CONCLUSIONS
RECOMMENDATIONS
ATTACHMENTS

Under each heading key in the list of topics you previously annotated with that heading's identification letter, arranging them in a logical order. If there are a lot of topics you may have to do this in two steps, first key-stroking the topics in random order and then rearranging them on screen. When you have finished, your writing outline will be ready and you can print a hard copy to use as a guide as you subsequently keystroke your report into the computer. If, as you write the report, you find you need to modify the outline or add a section to it, the changes are easy to make since you can quickly access the OUTLINE file, keystroke the alterations, and print a new copy.

Preparing to Write

When you handwrite a report, you normally give little thought to its final appearance during the writing stage; but when you keystroke a report you have to consider all the options that a typist normally looks after, such as line length, position of page numbers, indenting of the first line of each paragraph, and whether the report is to be single or double spaced. And you have to think of these factors *before* you start writing.

Establishing Keystroke Parameters

Having to define keystroke parameters is not as formidable as it sounds. Many commonly used features will have been built into the WP program as defaults and will automatically be taken into account unless you change them. Generally the default parameters are:

- The length of the typing line. In the program I work with (*Wordstar "Professional" 4.0*) the default is 65 characters, which provides a 6.5-inch printing line if the printer is set to produce 10 characters to the inch, i.e. "pica" size. But if I plan to print 12 characters to the inch—"elite" size, which I normally use—and still maintain a 6.5-inch printing line, I have to change the length of the typing line to 78 characters, otherwise the printed lines would be only 5.4 inches long.

- The number of lines each page is to hold. The default I am accustomed to is 55 lines.

- The width of each margin. The default normally positions the lines so that when printed they have an equal-size margin on both sides. If you are preparing a report that is to be bound within a folder, you may want to set a wider margin on the left side of the page to allow for a binding edge. In my program it is the dot command ".po" followed by a number. For example, ".po9" means that I want the printing to be offset nine columns to the right.

- The position of the page numbers. My program automatically positions page numbers at the foot of the page, centred three lines below the last line of text, at column 32. If I establish a 78-character typing line—which I normally do—I also have to identify that I want the page number to be in the middle of the line, at column 39, otherwise the printed page numbers will seem offset to the left. (The default for other systems may place the page numbers centred above the text or at the top-right corner flush with the right-hand margin.)

- Line spacing. In the program I am using the default is single spacing.
- Justification of the right-hand margin. For *unjustified* text, the right-hand margin is ragged like a page typed by a regular typewriter. For *justified* text, the spacing within each line is adjusted so that every line finishes exactly at the right-hand margin. Note, however, that there are two styles of justification: in one, extra spaces are provided only between the words; in the other, extra spaces are provided between the letters, which looks much more natural when the words are printed. The default in the program I use automatically justifies the text.
- Word hyphenation. You can choose where the hyphen should be placed in a word that extends beyond the right-hand margin, or allow the WP program to insert the hyphen where *it* defines the break should occur. The former is better, if you want to avoid some rather strange hyphenation, because the program cannot rationalize in its assessment of each word to determine which is the best place to break it. You will also have to identify whether you have to enable or disable the hyphenating option, because each WP program is set up differently.

Establishing Format Parameters

When you keystroke your own reports you also have to consider how you want each report to look when it is printed. These formatting factors were previously attended to by your typist. Now *you* have to decide:

- The number of blank lines between paragraphs. Normally one blank line is used for short, single-spaced reports. For formal reports and proposals, two blank lines should be left between paragraphs to create a more open effect. (Two blank lines are always inserted between paragraphs when the whole report is double spaced.)
- Whether the first line of each paragraph is to be indented. Generally, first lines tend not to be indented in modern correspondence and short reports. In long reports, the same tends to hold true, although there are variations. Whichever you do, be consistent within the same document.
- How you plan to indent subparagraphs. This seemingly innocuous factor is important because the manner in which subparagraphs and sub-subparagraphs are indented provides a visual clue to the reader as to how you have subordinated your ideas. Note how this subparagraph

is indented, and the subparagraphs before and after it: each is moved to the right as a complete block of information. Subsubparagraphs can be treated in exactly the same way, except that they are indented a double distance to the right.

- The types of headings you will use, and how you will differentiate between headings of varying levels. The three choices available to you are:

    1. HEADINGS ALL IN CAPITAL LETTERS, AND UNDERLINED

    2. HEADINGS ALL IN CAPITAL LETTERS, BUT NOT UNDERLINED

    3. Headings in Lowercase Letters, and Underlined

        (Note that the first letter of each principal word in lowercase headings is *capitalized*.)

By placing some headings in the centre of the page and some at the left margin, you can achieve six levels of headings. Remember, however, that centre-page headings predominate over side headings. The body of the formal report in chapter 8 offers a good example of how to use three levels of headings.

Planning for Illustrations

Although you do not have to make any specific keystroking plans for leaving spaces for illustrations and diagrams, you should keep them in mind as you write and be aware that you will be integrating them into the text during the editing stage. Your aim should be to place each illustration as close as possible to the text it supports, preferably on the same page. Here are three guidelines to follow:

1. Before writing, identify and list the illustrations you will be using. For each, note its horizontal and vertical dimensions, and specifically where it will be used. Enter a note about the illustration at the appropriate place in the outline.

2. If your WP system has graphics capabilities, and you can integrate the graphics with the text as you keystroke the report, prepare the illustration in a separate file. Note the file identification so you can call it up and insert it at the appropriate moment.

3. If your WP system does not have graphics capabilities, when you reach a point while keystroking the report where an illustration is to be inserted, make an entry identifying the illustration and its dimensions.

(This entry will be removed during the final editing stage, when illustrations are inserted manually into the hard copy.)

Planning for Reference/Bibliography Entries

As with illustrations, you should plan to insert your references to other documents or sources of information as you keystroke your report. This means some advance planning.

1. Decide whether you will be using a list of references or a bibliography to identify your documentation sources. (See chapter 11, pages 170-176, for further information.)

2. Create a REFRNCES file, and in it write your full list of reference or bibliography entries. (Refer to chapter 11 for guidelines for correct listing of information sources.) Print a hard copy and keep it beside you as you write.

3. Annotate the outline to identify where you expect references to source documents to occur, noting which item will be referred to.

4. As you keystroke the report, each time you need to refer to a source document key in the reference.

In some of the more sophisticated WP programs, you can create a bibliography, list of references, or footnotes as you keystroke your report. The program stores each entry as you keystroke it, and then presents the list arranged in the proper sequence and format at the end of the report or at the foot of the page.

Writing (Keystroking) the Report

Many professional people—all specialists in their fields—have a real problem getting the first words onto paper. For them, the computer is unlikely to prove an instant panacea and certainly will not loosen up a hesitant writing arm. The only answer to this problem is to change one's approach to writing, either on the computer or on paper. These five steps may help break the "writer's block" syndrome:

• Rather than consider the report as a single long file to be keystroked into the computer, think of it as a series of short files.

• Scan the outline and divide it into a series of separate self-contained topics. For each topic, assign a file title of no more than eight letters, such as INTRO (for introduction), INV-APPR (for investigation approach), and COM-ANAL (for comparative analysis).

- Start writing *anywhere*, except at the beginning. Scan the outline and identify which topics are most appealing or potentially most interesting, and write about them first.
- Avoid trying to keystroke a perfect first draft. Recognize that no one—not even a professional writer—expects to produce instantly usable words and sentences that require no further polishing.
- Keystroke with a minimum of editing. Try to achieve a momentum that will carry the writing along.

Let's look more closely at what these five steps imply. If you treat a report as one long, coherent document, and start writing at the beginning, you are going to be inhibited by the immensity of the task even before you keystroke one word into the computer. But if you consider each section of the report as a mini-report complete in itself—with an introductory section, a development in the middle, and a concluding section—the task will not seem nearly so forbidding. Additionally, you will be constructing a report that is cohesive from start to finish and coherent within each section.

Start by writing about a topic you are particularly familiar with, so that your knowledge of and interest in the topic will help you form the initial words, even if they are not quite what you planned to write. Say to yourself:

> "The first few sentences I write will not be nearly as good as I would like, but I will leave them there, on disk, without attempting to revise them now. I'll look at them again later, when I have a better handle on the overall approach I have taken in other parts."

Later on, when you do go back to revise them, you will find the correct words form in your mind much more readily.

Writing is a creative process that demands concentration and continuity. After several sentences or paragraphs have been written without interruption, it is common for a momentum to build that will see a writer keystroking rapidly and even mouthing the words aloud as he or she pounds them onto the keys. At such times the creative process is working at its utmost and any interruption can destroy it. If you continually stop to correct or revise what is on screen, you will prevent that momentum from developing.

For that reason you should keystroke a complete section of a report before you attempt to edit it, either on screen or on hard copy. If, as you keystroke, you suddenly realize how to correct a paragraph that previously dissatisfied you, do not go back to it. Instead, when you reach a comfortable break in what you are currently writing, type notes directly onto the screen describing what you want to do, or totally rewrite the paragraph right where you are. (You can insert a row of asterisks above and below the new sentences, so you can readily identify them.) When you are in the editing stage the revision can easily be copied into the correct place in the file.

Every few pages, stop for a moment to "save to disk" what you have already typed. This will prevent you from losing too much of your work if there is a sudden power-outage or CPU failure. (Such failures may be rare, but the anguish of discovering you have irretrievably lost many pages of careful keystroking has to be experienced only once for you to remember always to "save" your data at regular intervals.)

When you have completed writing your first section, you have to decide whether to review and edit it right away, before you start writing the next section, or simply keep it on file and continue writing the remaining sections. There is no preferred method; both are widely used. If you feel you have momentum and decide to continue writing, you may find it useful to print a hard copy so that you can glance over what you have already written, particularly if you need to correlate the information in one section with the information in another.

Some report writers who are accustomed to working with pencil and paper feel they are writing into a vacuum when they start keystroking. They see their freshly written sentences and paragraphs moving steadily up the screen, displaced at the bottom by their newly formed sentences. When there are some 20 lines on the screen (10 lines, if they are keystroking a double-spaced report) their first lines disappear out of sight at the top of the screen. True, they can recall any part of the report at any time, but the amount they can see is limited to a comparatively small 20-line "window." This visual limitation can be one of the most difficult obstacles to writing at a computer.

For that reason I recommend that newcomers to on-screen writing print a hard copy of their work whenever they begin to feel the "vacuum effect" of keystroking. However, you should consciously resist trying to correct or revise hard copy produced for this purpose; remember that you have printed it as a handy reference source, not as editing copy.

Checking (Editing) Your Own Words

You can edit (read and revise) a report stored on disk in two ways:

- You can do all the work directly on screen, without making a printout.
- You can print a hard copy and make your revisions in pencil, later transferring the changes on screen to the computer-stored report.

Most people are more comfortable working on hard copy, partly because they are accustomed to working with a pen or pencil in their hands, and partly because they can see the whole report and easily refer back and forth to the different report sections. The guidelines below assume that you edit on hard copy.

If you hesitate to make on-screen changes to your words because later you may have second thoughts, or you feel you might want to see the first draft again, remember that you do not destroy the first draft when you make the corrections. The first draft remains unchanged on disk, and you work on a *copy* that is brought into the computer's memory specifically for that purpose. And even when you save the revised draft to disk, the first draft is still retained on the disk as a backup (in most WP programs) and it remains there until further editing is done. As an added precaution you can also make a copy of any section or version of your report as you go along, assigning it a different file name, which you can store for as long as you feel you may need it.

Checking Spelling

One of the most convenient WP facilities available to writers who keystroke their own reports is the ability to have the computer check for spelling and typographical errors. The spell-check program works like this:

- The program has a dictionary of most common words in its memory, against which it compares all the words you have written.
- When the program encounters a word that is not in its memory, it notes the word and at the end of the check displays a list of all the "misspelled" words it has encountered.
- For each word in the list, the spell-check program then asks you to indicate whether you want to:

  1. fix the word (because you keystroked it incorrectly),

2. add the word to the dictionary (so that the program will not recognize it as an error next time), or

3. ignore the word (because you do not use it often enough to warrant placing it in the dictionary).

- The program then takes you to each word in the text that you flagged as needing fixing, and either corrects it automatically or lets you correct it.

Although each spell-check program has various additional features, those stated above are common to all programs.

Spell-check programs are not infallible, however. If you inadvertently type "their" when you mean to type "there," or misspell "principal" as "principle," the program will not flag the words as errors because all four words reside in its memory (you have to remember that it cannot recognize when you have used a word incorrectly). Consequently a spell-check program does not eliminate proofreading; it only simplifies it. And a final suggestion: if you do a spell-check before you start revising, remember that you should do a second spell-check after the revisions have been incorporated, in case you created further spelling or typographical errors while you were making the corrections.

Initial Proofreading

The first rule of editing is *not* to pick up a pencil right away and start correcting the words as you read them. There are two preliminary steps you should take:

1. Keep the draft of a report you have just finished keystroking out of sight until enough time has elapsed that you can review it with a fresh eye. Correcting your sentences and paragraphs immediately after you have finished writing them is an invitation to see what you *intended* to write rather than what you actually wrote; you will still be influenced by the enthusiasm and momentum of the moment, and hence tend to miss ambiguities, factual errors, and insipid constructions that you would pounce upon in another person's writing. With keystroking it is easy to keep a report out of sight until you are ready to read it: simply do not make a hard copy—then you will not be tempted to read it too soon.

2. The first time you read a section (or the whole report if it is short), read all the way through *without* a pen or pencil in your hand. Your

intent should be to view your work the way your readers will view it: as a continuous document read without stopping to make changes. This way, you will be able to check its overall continuity *before* you become too familiar with the individual parts.

Detailed Editing

Most people consider "editing" to mean checking that one's work is written well and has no grammatical or typographical errors. This is true, but it is only part of the picture. Proper editing means making a word-by-word check of a document to determine:

• its appropriateness,
• its coherence, completeness, correctness and conciseness, and
• the quality of the writing.

An experienced editor can check all of these factors concurrently. We—as inexperienced editors—would be wise to examine them separately.

Checking for Appropriateness.   This can be done during the initial read-through. It means stopping first to ask yourself the questions previously discussed in chapter 10 (see pages 156-168).

1. Who is my reader?
2. What is the purpose of my report?
3. Do I want to be informative or persuasive?

Keep the answers to these three questions continually in mind as you read. Check all the time that the tone and technical level are correct for the intended readers, and that you are providing the information they need—not too many details, yet not too few. If you are still unsure about the appropriateness of your writing, there is a second check you can make later (see "Obtaining an Objective Opinion" on page 214).

Checking for Coherence and Completeness.   These two factors can also be examined during the initial read-through. Checking for coherence means ensuring that there are logical connections between the different parts of the report, not just within the section you are currently editing. Checking for completeness means ensuring that *all* the information the reader needs has been transmitted. If you prepared a comprehensive outline and stuck to it as you wrote, then you can be reasonably sure that what you have written is complete.

Checking for Correctness.   Here you have to examine facts and figures to ensure they have been accurately transmitted from their source to the disk. It means meticulous checking of every detail in your report, particularly quantities, measurements, and times. When proofreading, especially on screen, we tend to pay attention to the words and *assume* the numbers are correct. Yet it is very easy to transpose a number when keystroking (writing, for example, 7596 when the correct number is 7956) and then not notice the error as one reads. This is particularly true of numbers buried in a sentence, like this:

> A check of the 7596 samples taken at the test site showed that
> 247 (3.1%) were contaminated.

Because we are checking the readability of the words, the numbers seem to fit in with the flow of the sentence. Yet a reader checking the calculation would discover that 3.1% of 7596 is 235, and would not know which of the three numbers in the sentence are correct. This does not mean you have to recalculate everything during the editing stage; it simply means going back to the source of your figures and checking that you keystroked them accurately. (Particular attention should be paid to quantities that appear within the sentences of a report, because you are more likely to check the accuracy of quantities that appear together in, for example, a table.)

Checking for Conciseness.   As you proofread you should be continually evaluating whether you have presented your information succinctly. There are two factors to consider:

- The tendency when keystroking to overwrite. The more efficient you are as a typist, the more likely you are to say too much. Keystroking is easy and, because you can see only so many words that you have written before they disappear off the top of the screen, you probably will write more about a topic than you would if you were writing with a pen on paper. Be aware of this idiosyncrasy and check that you have not become garrulous.

- The natural tendency to use clichés and words of low information content. As chapter 10 describes under the heading ''Avoid Clutter'' (see pages 165-168), it is a rare writer who does not occasionally use an expression that sounds nice but adds little to a sentence. Be aware that keystroking increases this tendency, and take particular care to check that you have not been too wordy.

If wordiness is a problem—and particularly a tendency to use big words—you can purchase a software program that will count the size of each word you have keystroked. It then provides you with a readout that compares your average word size against a "wordiness" scale. Several such programs are available, and more are regularly coming onto the market.

Checking for Good Language.   This is probably the most difficult factor to assess in your own writing. You should automatically check that you have used good grammar and proper punctuation. You should also check that you have used a definite, informative, readable style in which the active voice is more predominant than the passive voice (see pages 162-164), and the subordination of ideas is readily apparent. For more information on these aspects, refer to a standard handbook of English (there are many available, typically the *Prentice-Hall Handbook for Writers*).

Checking for Spelling and Typographical Errors.   Although you have already passed your keystroked report through a spell-check program, you still need to proofread it for typographical and spelling errors that the program did not pick up, such as omitting the "d" from the end of "formalized" (which the program would recognize as "formalize" and not flag as an error) or accidentally keystroking "continual" and "accept" when you meant to write "continuous" and "except." Such proofreading calls for word-by-word scrutiny and is best done as a separate check during which you search *solely* for typos. It is also difficult to do thoroughly on screen.

Take a clean sheet of paper or a ruler and slide it slowly down the hard copy one line at a time. Pause as each line becomes visible and read it slowly and carefully, one word at a time, keeping the next line covered so that you will not be tempted to skip along quickly and start reading it. At the same time check that the commas, colons, semicolons, and periods have been inserted correctly. This line-by-line scrutiny may be slow, but it is effective because you examine individual words without being influenced by complete thoughts.

Mark each error clearly. Rather than just write a careful correction, draw a bold circle around the error so that you will notice it when you again refer to the page as you make changes on screen. Avoid the practice of proofreading beside the computer terminal and making each correction as you find it, because you will lose the dedicated concentration you need for proofreading. For added visibility, use a coloured pen or pencil; red or green is ideal.

Making Corrections On Line

This is the easiest part of the editing process. Simply bring the report—
or a section of the report—back on screen and carefully work through it,
incorporating all the changes you have marked on the hard copy. Then,
if enough changes have been made to warrant it, again process the report
through the spell-check program. Finally, save the revised report to disk
(remember that the computer will retain your original version as a backup
copy, in case you need to go back to it).

Doing a Second (or Subsequent) Edit

When all the improvements and corrections have been made, you are ready
to do your second edit. This time you have to check only three factors:

1. That the report reads smoothly and coherently, and says what you want
   it to say to the readers you have in mind.
2. That all the changes you identified during the first edit have been correctly implemented.
3. That you have not inadvertently created any spelling or typographical
   errors while making the corrections.

I suggest you read the report twice: once for readability (item 1, above),
and once for accuracy (items 2 and 3). This time, however, you do not
have to make a line-by-line check of the whole report, as you did previously. You can limit your check to those areas where you keystroked some
changes.

Again key in any further changes and check for readability and accuracy.
Remember, however, that when you save the report containing the second set of revisions, many WP systems—and particularly those using
limited-storage floppy disks—keep only the most recent version as a
backup. If you wish also to keep your original first draft you should assign
it a different file name or make a copy of it, which should be done *before*
you bring the report back on screen to make the second set of revisions.

How long should you continue reading the report and making changes?
Continue until you feel the report is an effective conveyor of information,
keeping these two guidelines in mind:

- If the report is going to an important client and a major contract or project
  depends on how it is received, then you should spend considerable time
  polishing it and you should probably read it several times before you
  issue it.

- If the report is for in-house use and is fairly routine, then you probably need to edit it only once.

Reports that fall between these guidelines will probably need only two or three edits.

Obtaining an Objective Opinion

One of the problems of editing your own work—whether handwritten or keystroked—is being able to view it objectively. Often, familiarity with the subject can blind you to your report's deficiencies. Consequently, when a report is particularly important you would be wise to ask a disinterested person to read it and give you an objective opinion of how well it achieves its purpose. The reader will probably have to be someone who works where you do, but it should be a person who is no more familiar with your project than the intended audience will be and who can view what you have written without bias. It should also be someone who will give you an *honest* opinion of your report: we all like politely phrased words complimenting us on our writing prowess, but when looking for constructive criticism polite words are not much help.

When asking a reviewer to give you an opinion, always explain first:

- Why the report needs to be reviewed.
- Who the ultimate reader is.
- What impact or effect you want the report to have on the reader.
- What aspects of the report particularly need the reviewer's attention. (You don't want the reviewer to think he or she is being asked to proof-read the report, if what you really want is an opinion on the report's persuasiveness or tone.)
- How soon you need the reviewer's comments.

Ideally, write what you want the reviewer to do at the top of a sheet of 8½ × 11-inch paper and clip it to the front of the report. Ask the reviewer to write rather than tell you his or her opinion and suggestions, either on the sheet of paper or on the report itself. A spoken statement such as ''Sounds good to me, though you had better fix up a bit of wool-liness on page seven'' is too vague to be of much help. And when you receive the reviewer's comments, welcome them even if you disagree with them; try not to be defensive if the reviewer says things about your writing that make you feel uncomfortable!

Desktop Publishing
and How it May Affect You

In the early 1980s the expression "desktop publishing" (DTP) was little more than a buzzword for what most people considered to be an expensive toy, even a passing fad. But in less than a decade DTP had blossomed into an industry that clearly would change the way organizations in both the private and public sectors prepared their publications for printing. The key lay in two significant factors inherent in DTP: the ability to maintain in-house control of the entire pre-printing process, from writing right up to the moment the document is sent to the printer as "camera-ready" copy; and the substantial cost savings. An article in the January 1987 *Newsletter* of the IEEE Professional Communication Society describes how the Society's New Communication Technology Committee used DTP to prepare a technical training manual for printing:

> To speed up production and cut costs, the 350 pages were typed
> on a personal computer and printed on a laser printer...using
> Times Roman as the typeface.[1]

The author cites four advantages that accrued:

- The high quality of product and the simplicity with which it was achieved.
- The ability to retain personal control of layout and presentation.
- The time saved, because proofreading was reduced to a minimum.
- The very much lower cost. With traditional typesetting the cost would have been between $12 and $18 per page for typesetting and page paste-up. With laser desktop typesetting the cost was reduced to under $5 for each camera-ready page. If the pages had been pure narrative rather than a complex arrangement of tables and boxes...the cost would have been reduced to under $3 per page.[2]

Faced with results like these, it's no wonder that managements are jumping quickly into DTP. Because DTP will affect you markedly as a writer of reports, proposals, instruction manuals, and brochures, this section discusses some of the factors you will have to consider. Remember, however, that the DTP industry is probably the fastest-developing sector of the microcomputer business, and is changing so rapidly that new developments undoubtedly will quickly supersede some of the developments described here.

Implications for the Writer

As a report writer who keystrokes his or her own reports, you will be accustomed to editing your own words and being responsible for creating the format and appearance of the report (see pages 202-205). But in DTP you may also be responsible for *designing* the publication.

Reports printed on letter-quality printers or "equivalent to letter quality" printers are printed according to the familiar typewriter convention and so pose no problem from a design viewpoint. Reports and publications prepared using DTP facilities, however, demand a knowledge of typesetting, page layout, and publication design, which does pose a problem.

In their zeal to achieve lower costs, managements may overlook that by installing DTP equipment they are removing the middleman in the publication process, the designer. Previously, if an organization planned to typeset a particular report or sales leaflet, they would have staff members write it and then they would take it to a commercial designer or to a printing house with a designer on staff. The writer would have no input into the design other than possibly to sketch an idea of how he or she visualized the document. With DTP, the document leaves its originator in "camera-ready" form when it goes to the printer. Unless the organization employs a designer or technical editor knowledgeable of design criteria, the onus for presentation rests entirely on the report writer.

While a full description of design conventions is beyond the scope of this book, there are some factors you should research:

- The typefaces that are available and which ones will be most suitable for a particular document.
- Which sizes of type should be used for different pieces of information.
- How to use different typefaces within the same document (generally, typefaces should not be mixed indiscriminately).
- How much an illustration can be reduced to fit a space without losing its usefulness.
- How to screen a photograph for a particular purpose or printing process.
- When and how to use colour, and the increase in cost that colour printing will incur.
- How to select a printing process and printer for a particular product.

As a report writer new to keystroking, and particularly desktop publishing, you would be unlikely to know more than the rudiments of publication design. For that reason, initially you would be wise to seek advice from a graphics designer.

References

1. "NCT Committee Leaps into Desktop Publishing." IEEE Professional Communication Society *Newsletter*, 30: 1, January 1987.
2. IEEE *Newsletter*.

15

Guidelines for Working with a Report Production Team

A report writer's work is not over when he or she hands in a handwritten draft for typing. From that moment on, the report writer becomes part of a report production team, with each member being responsible for certain aspects of the report. The report writer has overriding responsibility, not only for the information conveyed in the report, but also for the quality of language and the report's appearance.

A report production team can be composed of as few as two persons or as many as seven or eight, or even more. In a small company the production team may comprise only the report writer and the typist, with one of them making copies of the report on an office copier. In a large company the production team may include one or two illustrators, two or more typists, a printer, and an editor or publications supervisor, all in addition to the report writer. (When the team has an editor, responsibility for correctness of language and the report's appearance usually shifts to that person. The report writer retains responsibility for correctness of information, and should share some responsibility for correctness of language.) If more than one person writes a report and there is no editor, one of the writers is normally appointed coordinating writer.

The impression that readers gain of the report writer and the company or organization he or she works for is influenced directly by what they see and read. Words poorly centred on the title page, typing errors, misspelled words, unevenly positioned page numbers, and grammatically incorrect sentences create an image of a sloppy worker employed by an organization which produces a low-quality product or service. On the other hand, good language and crisp, clear typing neatly positioned on every page convey the image of a confident report writer employed by a highly professional organization.

Being responsible for the production of your own report means working cooperatively with the remaining team members, principally the persons who will type, illustrate, and print it. The guidelines listed in this final chapter suggest ways for achieving a harmonious atmosphere. They are just as applicable when a report is prepared using desktop publishing methods.

Your first step should be to set up a schedule, and then to meet with all the persons who will be involved in the report to check that the dates you have allowed for each stage are realistic for the amount of work required. The schedule may be a simple list showing proposed dates of completion for each stage, or it can be a form which travels with the report, as illustrated in Figure 15-1.

	REPORT PRODUCTION CONTROL SHEET				
Step	Action	Planned Compl Date	Action by	Init.	Date Step Completed
1	Write first draft	Feb 16	Author	DML.	Feb 15
2	Type first draft	Feb 26	Typist		
3	Check typed draft	Feb 28	Author		
4	Prepare illustrations	Feb 28	Drafting		
5	Check illustrations	Mar 1	Author		
6	Check draft & illus.	Mar 4	Supervisor		
7	Make final revisions	Mar 6	Author		
8	Type second draft*		Typist		
9	Check second draft*		Author		
10	Type final report	Mar 11	Typist		
11	Check final report	Mar 12	Author		
12	Print report copies	Mar 15	Printing		

* Steps 8 & 9 apply only if many changes are made to the first draft.

Fig. 15-1. *A report schedule to accompany a report.*

Working with Typists

Always give typists clear guidelines. Unless you tell them exactly what you have in mind they will type your words in the format they are accustomed to, which may not coincide with your ideas. Typists who are using a standard electric typewriter need to know:

1. The size of the typing area or, alternatively, the width of margins (e.g. 30 mm minimum each side and at the top of the page, with 40 mm at the bottom to allow for the page number).
2. Whether the report is to have single-, 1½-, or double-line spacing.
3. The number of blank lines between paragraphs.
4. Whether the first line of each paragraph is to be indented, or the paragraphs are to be typed solid against the left-hand margin. (Marjorie Franckel's progress report on page 42 is the only report in this text which has been typed with the first line of each paragraph indented; all other reports have been typed "full block.")
5. Whether the typed original or a printed copy will be sent to the addressee. (If the original is to be sent, then the typist cannot use much white corrective fluid to erase errors; if printed copies are to be distributed, and the original is to remain with the report writer, then correcting fluid can be used.)
6. The type-style and pitch you prefer. You have a choice of type size if the typewriter has dual pitch (i.e. 10 (pica) or 12 (elite) characters to the inch).
7. Whether what is being typed is a draft or the final version.
8. Where spaces are to be left for illustrations, and the exact amount of space required.
9. The date the typing is required.

You also need to work out who is to proofread the typed work. Proofreading should be done by two people, with one reading aloud to the other. This can be two typists, or yourself and a typist. Proofreading alone is both tedious and prone to error: it is much too easy not to notice a missing line or phrase.

Working with a Word Processing System

Working with a typist who is using a word processing (WP) system is similar to working with a typist who is using a standard electric typewriter, but very much faster. The main advantage of a WP system is that, once the first draft of the report has been typed and a copy printed out, you can revise the hard copy, have the typist incorporate your changes, and print out a second draft within only minutes. A secondary advantage accrues if you can type well enough to keystroke your first draft directly into the computer rather than write it out laboriously by hand, as described in chapter 14.

Most of the guidelines you would give to a typist who is using a standard electric typewriter are equally valid for a typist who is using a WP system. The main differences are:

- the WP typist needs to know if the right-hand margin is to be justified (that is, if every line is to be the same length), and how wide the lines of type are to be,
- there is no need to use correcting fluid (previous guideline 5), and
- there may be a wider range of typefaces and sizes to choose from.

Working with Illustrators and Draftspersons

Good communication is extremely important between a report writer and an illustrator or draftsperson (who for clarity I shall refer to jointly as "illustrator"). If the illustrations in your report are to complement the words you have written, your illustrator needs to know something about the topic, the purpose of the report, who the reader(s) will be, and what aspects need to be emphasized.

There are five guidelines for effective communication between yourself and the illustrator:

1. Explain the purpose of the report, and of each illustration.
2. Discuss how each illustration is to support your words (give the illustrator a draft copy of your report to read), and describe what parts are most important. If possible, sketch each illustration as best you can, and then give the sketch to the illustrator so he or she can visualize what you have in mind.
3. Provide accurate vertical and horizontal dimensions for each illustration. If the illustration is to be preceded or followed by typing, allow sufficient space between the illustration and the text, so that the page does not look crowded.
4. Be sure to allow the illustrator plenty of time. Quote an "illustration completion date" (preferably in writing), and obtain the illustrator's

assurance that the date can be met. Never say you want your illustrations ASAP (as soon as possible).

5. Discuss oversize drawings and determine how much they will be reduced photographically, so that the illustrator will know not to make construction lines too light.

Working with a Printer

Most business and technical reports are printed in-house, or by a local "quick copy" service. In both cases the reports are duplicated on an office copier if only a few copies are required, or on an offset press if more than, say, 50 copies are required. (Only rarely is a report taken to a professional printer. Corporate annual reports would be a typical example.) If your report is printed in-house and the production run is short, you or your typist are likely to make the copies on a centrally located office copier. If your organization has its own print shop, or if you use a copy service, then you should discuss the job with the person who does the printing.

Guidelines for working with a printer are:

1. See the printer before the final typing and illustrating are done, and discuss the report. Find out what equipment the printer has, and if there are any special requirements or limitations (e.g. whether the printer can reduce a large drawing photographically, and print paragraphs or drawings which have been glued onto the typed original without creating shadow lines). Mention the date you plan to bring the job in, and ask how long the printing will take.

2. If the report is large or many copies are required, visit several printers and ask for cost estimates. Be sure to give the same requirements to each printer (e.g. number of pages and number of copies, how many photographs are being used, and whether the printer is to collate and bind the report).

3. When you take the job in for printing, write clear, complete instructions to the printer and clip or pin them to the job. Your instructions should include
    • number of copies required,
    • colour of ink to be used,
    • weight of paper (e.g. 20 lb bond),
    • size of paper (e.g. 8½ × 11 in.),
    • whether the report is to be printed on one or both sides of the paper,

- where photographs and drawings are to be inserted (they usually travel separately, in an envelope),
- whether the whole job is to be reduced photographically, and by how much (stated as a percentage: "Reduce by 10%" or "Reduce to 85%"),
- whether the job is to be collated and bound, and the type of binding required,
- any special instructions, and
- the date you require the printed report.

4. If the report is at all complex, make a mock-up showing how the finished product should appear. Use the correct number of blank sheets of paper, fold them once, and staple them together to form a booklet. Open up the booklet and write a descriptive word on each page to show what should be printed there. If a page is to be left blank, write "BLANK PAGE" on it. The printer will use the booklet to determine what to print on each page, and to assemble the sheets in the correct sequence.

Working with Management

Unless your company employs a full-time technical editor, your draft reports will travel upward through the chain of command, with someone at each level adding, deleting, or changing words according to his or her whims. Unless you are very lucky, the report you receive back from management may not look like the document you wrote.

You can avoid some of this frustration by going to your manager or immediate supervisor and asking for guidelines. Tell your manager that you need to know:

- Who the primary reader is, who the secondary readers are likely to be, and who is most likely to use the information you supply, or take action as a result of your report.
- If you can use the pyramid technique (main message up front) for *all* of your reports, regardless of whether they contain good or bad news.
- If you can use the first person ("I" or "we") in your reports.
- If you can use the more emphatic active voice, rather than stick to the dull, less interesting passive voice.

Finally, when you submit your draft report for evaluation, try to send a copy which is absolutely clean (i.e. has no pencilled or ink alterations, or ragged typing corrections). A rough-looking report invites the reviewer to make more corrections, whereas a clean copy tends to inhibit the evaluator from marking up the report. As a second level of assurance, try attaching a sheet of pink paper to the front of the report, on which you have printed a request for report reviewers to make their suggestions *on the pink sheet*, rather than mark up the clean original. When reviewers have to spend time writing and cross-referencing every suggestion, they tend to write only the important ones.

Index